Fundamental S...

The story of the kinds of atoms has been long in composition, with many minds and hands putting it together. The ancients knew and recognized some of the elements, such as gold, silver, copper, etc., found in their native state. Others, even some of the most common, long remained hidden, in disguise of some other element or in the crudeness of early chemistry.

There are just so many kinds of matter out of which the universe is made. Man has been able to discover 102 chemical elements—some of which he has created for a very momentary existence, and others like hydrogen and helium which seem to hold a heavy and stable majority in the universe. Some of these elements have been found or created in only the few years after the great atomic-energy push. There are hundreds of varieties of these elements—isotopes they are called—many artificially radioactive and not found in nature.

An outline of the elements, such as follows in these pages, is needed by anyone who attempts to work with them or understand them. This story is unfinished, although it is more nearly complete today than in the recent past. The blank holes in the periodic table are filled. Chemists may add to the elements known, but not with the speed, precision and practicality with which the dawn of our atomic age added neptunium, plutonium, americium, curium, berkelium, californium, einsteinium, fermium, mendelevium and 102.

The present frontier of the chemical elements lies in the mystery of what composes them. Just what more fundamental particles make them up and what laws and forces keep their nuclei together is the prime question of physical science. Scientists are trying to pry loose the answer with cosmic rays and gigantic accelerators.

The chemistry of the elements has some blank pages to be filled and some figures to change in the future. To give individuality to the many names in today's list of elements, and provide a guide to the varied literature about them, is the purpose of this introduction to the chemical elements.

PERIODIC TABLE OF THE ELEMENTS

Compiled by the Radiation Laboratory
of the University of California

1	2	3	4	5	6	7	8	9	10	11	12	13	14	15	16	17	18
1 H 1.0080																	2 He 4.003
3 Li 6.940	4 Be 9.013											5 B 10.82	6 C 12.011	7 N 14.008	8 O 16.000	9 F 19.00	10 Ne 20.183
11 Na 22.991	12 Mg 24.32											13 Al 26.98	14 Si 28.09	15 P 30.975	16 S 32.066	17 Cl 35.457	18 A 39.944
19 K 39.100	20 Ca 40.08	21 Sc 44.96	22 Ti 47.90	23 V 50.95	24 Cr 52.01	25 Mn 54.94	26 Fe 55.85	27 Co 58.94	28 Ni 58.71	29 Cu 63.54	30 Zn 65.38	31 Ga 69.72	32 Ge 72.60	33 As 74.91	34 Se 78.96	35 Br 79.916	36 Kr 83.80
37 Rb 85.48	38 Sr 87.63	39 Y 88.92	40 Zr 91.22	41 Nb 92.91	42 Mo 95.95	43 Tc	44 Ru 101.1	45 Rh 102.91	46 Pd 106.4	47 Ag 107.880	48 Cd 112.41	49 In 114.82	50 Sn 118.70	51 Sb 121.76	52 Te 127.61	53 I 126.91	54 Xe 131.30
55 Cs 132.91	56 Ba 137.36	57-71 La Series	72 Hf 178.50	73 Ta 180.95	74 W 183.86	75 Re 186.22	76 Os 190.2	77 Ir 192.2	78 Pt 195.09	79 Au 197.0	80 Hg 200.61	81 Tl 204.39	82 Pb 207.21	83 Bi 208.99	84 Po	85 At	86 Rn
87 Fr	88 Ra 226.03	89-103 Ac Series	(104)	(105)	(106)	(107)	(108)										

Lanthanide Series														
57 La 138.92	58 Ce 140.13	59 Pr 140.92	60 Nd 144.27	61 Pm	62 Sm 150.35	63 Eu 152.0	64 Gd 157.26	65 Tb 158.93	66 Dy 162.51	67 Ho 164.94	68 Er 167.27	69 Tm 168.94	70 Yb 173.04	71 Lu 174.99

Actinide Series														
89 Ac 227.04	90 Th 232.05	91 Pa 231.05	92 U 238.04	93 Np 237.06	94 Pu	95 Am	96 Cm	97 Bk	98 Cf	99 E	100 Fm	101 Mv	102	(103)

HELEN MILES DAVIS

with revisions by
Glenn T. Seaborg

The Chemical
Elements

| Science Service | • | Washington |
| Ballantine Books | • | New York |

Library of Congress Catalog Card No. 59-8991

Printed in the United States of America

Science Service, Inc.
1719 N St., N.W., Washington 6, D. C.

BALLANTINE BOOKS, INC.
101 Fifth Ave., New York 3, N. Y.

CONTENTS

The Chemical Elements

About This Book

The author, Helen Miles Davis, died in 1957 while this second edition of CHEMICAL ELEMENTS was in preparation. Dr. Glenn T. Seaborg—Nobelist in chemistry, now chancellor of the University of California at Berkeley, formerly director of the Radiation Laboratory, discoverer of transuranium elements—kindly consented to revise the text. To him and to his colleague, Dr. B. G. Harvey, our thanks for this cooperation.

Helen Miles Davis was editor of *Chemistry* magazine, published by Science Service, from 1944 to 1957. In appreciative recognition of her long service to the popularization of science since the beginnings of Science Service, it is hoped that this book, which is her creation, will be a lasting remembrance.

WATSON DAVIS
Director, Science Service.

The Chemical Elements

→ ELEMENTS are those substances which go through chemical manipulation without being resolved into simpler structures. They make up the distinct varieties of matter of which the universe is composed.

One hundred and two elements are now known, from hydrogen, the lightest, to man-made element 102, the heaviest and most recent. There are believed to be no gaps representing unknown elements in this list.

The neutron, since it is a material particle, may be included in the list of elements and assigned atomic number zero. Its properties place it in the group of inert elements which form no chemical compounds.

Matter is made up of the elements. An element may exist alone and uncombined. This is often the case with metals. The oxygen and the nitrogen of the air are also uncombined elements.

In most substances, the elements occur in combination with one another. Some elements, of which carbon is the outstanding example, form many compounds of complex structure. Some form only a few compounds. The inert gases form no compounds at all.

An atom is the unit quantity of each element. Its behavior displays the characteristic properties which distinguish that element from all the others.

Atoms of all the elements are made up of standard interchangeable parts, protons, neutrons and electrons. The differences between the elements are due to the number and arrangement of these sub-nuclear particles.

Although such particles are too small to be seen, their existence is deduced from direct evidence. Electrical phenomena are caused by these particles, and can be used to give information about them.

The proton is the atom of hydrogen, the lightest element, in a particular state of electrification. This results in the proton having a unit charge of positive electricity.

The neutron is a particle very similar to the proton in size and mass, but in an electrically neutral state. It can be studied by its effect on other substances.

The electron is a particle of electricity itself. Although it is thought of as the unit of electrical energy, certain of its manifestations are consistent with the idea that it also has some of the properties of matter, including the ability to spin on its axis. At this level the dividing line between matter and energy vanishes.

Other Subatomic Particles

Other subatomic particles have been found by physicists exploring the records left on their measuring devices.

The positron or antielectron (to be distinguished from the proton) is of the same dimensions as the electron, but with a positive electric charge instead of the electron's negative one.

The antimatter equivalents of the neutron and the proton were recently discovered. The difference between these particles of antimatter and particles of ordinary matter is that these antiparticles are converted into other forms of matter and energy on contact with ordinary matter. The apparent existence of this symmetry in nature has caused much speculation about the existence of star galaxies composed of antimatter, whose atoms consist of nuclei of antineutrons and antiprotons surrounded by clouds of positrons. The light coming from such stars would be identical to that from stars composed of ordinary matter; the only way astronomers could detect antimatter in space would be through the energy released if it collided with normal matter.

The terms "positive" and "negative" were applied arbitrarily, very early in the history of electricity. There is some evidence that a different set of terms would be helpful in visualizing subatomic phenomena. Many phenomena would be explained equally well by assuming one kind of electricity, that now called "negative", and considering "positive" electricity as its lack.

Discovery of the positron places a difficulty in the way of describing electricity in terms of one kind of particle. Yet the positron differs from the electron in being very scarce and having a very fleeting life.

Mesons

Studies of cosmic rays which originate in distant space resulted in the discovery of mesons. These particles are formed by the interation of cosmic rays with atomic nuclei and have some remarkable properties: they may have a positive, a negative, or no charge at all; most mesons have masses between those of the electron and the proton, although some (known as hyperons) are apparently heavier than the proton. All have a very short existence, being converted into other forms of matter and energy very rapidly. The production of artificial mesons has been made possible by the development of high-energy accelerators. Even though the energies of artificial mesons are much less than those appearing in nature, the ability to produce mesons in considerable number is a great advance in physical science.

All tentative speculations about little-known particles in the subatomic field point up the limitations of our senses. The remarkable thing is that so much information has been obtained. Glimpses into the subatomic world can sometimes be had by using special properties of one element or another.

Electrically charged particles can be observed because they affect the silver chloride of a photographic plate just as light does. When the plate is developed, the paths the particles have followed show up as lines. These lines are bent when the particles have passed between the poles of a magnet. By using a thick layer of photographic emulsion a three-dimensional record of the path can be obtained. The thick layer of emulsion can be cut into thin slices to study the track in more detail.

By varying the strength of the magnetic field between the poles, the particles can be made to change their courses. The curve of the track in the photographic plate then shows the velocity, and hence the energy, with which the particle that made it was travelling.

The mutual effect of the travelling particle and the varying magnetic field is the principle on which the cyclotron is built.

The familiar tricks of static electricity—the charge built up when a non-conductor is rubbed, the jump of a spark across an insulating gap or the leaking away of the charge when the system is grounded—are also used to study subatomic phenomena. They have evolved into such instruments as the Van de Graaff generator and the Geiger counter.

Atoms send out other communications, besides electrical signals. When compounds of many elements are heated, or when they are vaporized in an electric spark, light is given off which can be analyzed by a spectroscope.

The series of colored lines into which that instrument resolves the light is so distinctive that it can often prove the presence of one element in a mixture of many.

Among the Rare Earths, whose separation was long the despair of analytical chemists, the spectrum lines furnished proof of discovery of several of the individual elements.

Recognition of lines characteristic of the elements came long before the discovery of any regularity in spectral lines.

X-ray Spectra

It was not until the spectra made with X-rays were photographed and studied that the rhythm of certain groups of lines was recognized. These groups occur in the spectra of all elements, but shift to a different part of the spectrum as the mass of the elements increases.

With this key, the order of the elements was standardized. The problem caused by irregularities in the atomic mass of certain elements was settled, although not completely explained until later. The idea that all the elements are in some way built up of the same fundamental stuff was strengthened.

Out of the measurement of spectrum lines of the elements came the formulation of wave mechanics. With the newer mathematics as a tool, and the spectrum lines as evidence, a great deal has been learned about the way the successively heavier elements are built up out of subatomic particles.

The way similar chemical properties among the elements recur in periodic fashion gave the first clue to relationships among the elements. Mendeleeff, whose formulation of the Periodic Table was based on empirical data, was sure that the regular recurrence of similar properties among the elements when they are arranged in the order of their atomic masses represented a fundamental fact about them. He insisted that atomic masses which would place elements in the wrong groups must be wrong. He predicted the properties of elements needed to fill out his table, and lived to see three of his predictions fulfilled by the discovery of elements with the properties he expected for them.

A few pairs of elements persistently seemed to have the wrong atomic masses, no matter how carefully the analyses were made. These irregularities, it is now known, are due to mixtures of isotopes of different masses. The evidence of the X-ray spectra place such pairs of elements in the right order to correspond with their chemical properties. The rank of the elements as determined by the spectra is referred to as the atomic number. Except for the few irregularities mentioned, the order of elements by atomic number is the same as that by atomic mass.

Atom Structure

The periodic variation in the properties of the elements with increase in their masses is due to recurring similarity in the structure of their atoms.

Each atom is composed of a central nucleus surrounded by one or more electrons, a structure often likened to that of the solar system. Electrical forces hold the electrons, which are the units of electricity and have a negative charge, in their orbits around the positively charged nucleus.

In the case of hydrogen, the nucleus of the atom is one proton. Around it one electron revolves. The mass of the proton is 1845 times as great as that of the electron.

"Heavy hydrogen," also known as deuterium, has a nucleus consisting of one proton and one neutron. The neutron is a particle similar in size and mass to the proton. This makes the atomic mass of deuterium 2.

The nucleus of every atom is made up of protons and neutrons. A special kind of force holds these particles together. Its disruption releases atomic energy and results in transmutation of one element into another.

Isotopes

Elements whose nuclei have the same number of protons have practically identical properties, regardless of the number of neutrons. The neutrons merely add to the atomic mass. Such elements, alike in every property except mass, are called isotopes.

Some isotopes are radioactive, some are stable. Hydrogen has a radioactive isotope, tritium, besides the stable one, deuterium. Tritium has one proton and two neutrons in its nucleus. Its atomic mass is 3. Its symbol is written $_1H^3$.

The subscript number before the letter symbol represents the atomic number of the element, which is the number of protons in the nucleus. The superscript number after the letter symbol represents the atomic mass of the isotope. Thus deuterium is written $_1H^2$ or $_1D^2$. Ordinary hydrogen is $_1H^1$.

Chemical energy results from the activities of the electrons which circle the nucleus. These electrons may be pictured as tiny planets, each spinning on its axis, occupying orbits whose paths outline a series of concentric shells surrounding the nucleus of the atom. The mathematical formulæ of wave mechanics explain the conditions for the existence of these shells.

The attraction between the positive electrical forces of the protons in the nucleus and the negative charge on each electron revolving around the nucleus holds the atom together, but the electrons in the outer orbits are less firmly held than those nearer the center. The balance between the forces results also in some configurations of electrons being extremely stable while others are much less so.

The chemical properties of the elements depend upon these configurations. Eight electrons in the outside shell of any atom cause the inner forces to be so well balanced that the resulting element forms no compounds with other elements. Such are the inert elements of Group Zero in the Periodic Table.

Valence

Addition of one more proton to the nucleus and one more electron outside the complete shell of 8 accounts for the great chemical activity of the alkali metals of Group I. The fact that there is only one electron in the outside shell accounts for the valence, or combining power, of one, which is characteristic of those metals.

Two electrons in the outer shell give the Alkaline Earth metals of Group II their valences of two, and so on until, with Group IV, more stability is reached with a half-filled shell. With still more electrons, the character of the compounds formed emphasizes the lack of electrons to make up a new stable shell of 8, instead of the surplus over the earlier shell.

Whereas elements with a few excess electrons outside a closed shell have the property of alkalinity or basicity, (Groups

I, II, and III), those lacking three, two or one electrons to complete their shells form acids, (Groups V, VI and VII).

The halogens of Group VII are strongly acidic, and combine directly with alkaline elements to form stable salts. In general within a group, alkalinity increases with atomic weight, and acidity decreases. Thus, among the halogens, fluorine and chlorine combine more avidly with basic elements than do bromine and iodine. Metallic qualities also increase with atomic weight, and this is again illustrated in the halogen group. Iodine is an example of an element in transistion toward metallic properties, and astatine is reported to be still more metallic.

Elements of the acidic type frequently combine to form radicals, closely linked combinations of atoms which also form salts with alkaline elements. Nitrates, sulfates and chlorates are salts of this type, and many heavier elements also form such compounds. Oxides of many metals, for example chromium, are frequently referred to as acids, and indeed, when in solution in water, they behave as true acids. Oxygen is not the only element which joins in such radicals. Sulfur forms a whole series of such acids, which are distinguished by the prefix sulfo-, or sometimes thio-.

The general theory of compound formation holds that there is always a tendency toward the formation of shells of eight electrons as the outer layer of atomic systems. When an atom of sodium, with one excess electron, joins an atom of chlorine, with seven electrons, the eight electrons they have between them thus make up a closed shell and the resulting salt is a compound of considerable chemical stability.

Like many pictures of phenomena at the atomic level, this is an over-simplification. It does not go into the gain and loss of electrons when compounds are ionized in solution, or in air when electrically charged, or how elements form series of compounds with a change in their valences. These phenomena are real. They can be measured easily by electrical instruments. It is better to learn the phenomena by actual experience first, and then fit the phenomena into imaginary pictures as a memory device than to become deeply involved with theory before making the acquaintance of the actual chemicals.

The concept of electron shells, has, however, simplified the explanation of the periodic change of properties among the elements, both vertically in the Periodic Table, and horizontally from group to group.

The general formula for the number of electrons in each shell is $2n^2$, where n increases by whole numbers from one shell to the next. In the K shell, $n = 1$, and the number of electrons in the shell is $2 \times 1^2 = 2$. In the L shell, $n=2$ and the number of electrons is $2 \times 2^2 = 8$. Similarly, in the complete M shell, $2 \times 3^2 = 18$, and, in the complete N shell, $2 \times 4^2 = 32$. Beyond this, the known elements do not fill the shells theoretically possible according to this formula.

List of Elements Showing Grouping of Electrons in Shells

Shells		K	L		M			N				O				P				Q
Sub-Groups		1s	2s	2p	3s	3p	3d	4s	4p	4d	4f	5s	5p	5d	5f	6s	6p	6d	6f	7s
1	H	1																		
2	He	2																		
3	Li	2	1																	
4	Be	2	2																	
5	B	2	2	1																
6	C	2	2	2																
7	N	2	2	3																
8	O	2	2	4																
9	F	2	2	5																
10	Ne	2	2	6																
11	Na	2	2	6	1															
12	Mg	2	2	6	2															
13	Al	2	2	6	2	1														
14	Si	2	2	6	2	2														
15	P	2	2	6	2	3														
16	S	2	2	6	2	4														
17	Cl	2	2	6	2	5														
18	A	2	2	6	2	6														
19	K	2	2	6	2	6		1												
20	Ca	2	2	6	2	6		2												
21	Sc	2	2	6	2	6	1	2												
22	Ti	2	2	6	2	6	2	2												
23	V	2	2	6	2	6	3	2												
24	Cr	2	2	6	2	6	5	1												
25	Mn	2	2	6	2	6	5	2												
26	Fe	2	2	6	2	6	6	2												
27	Co	2	2	6	2	6	7	2												
28	Ni	2	2	6	2	6	8	2												
29	Cu	2	2	6	2	6	10	1												
30	Zn	2	2	6	2	6	10	2												
31	Ga	2	2	6	2	6	10	2	1											
32	Ge	2	2	6	2	6	10	2	2											
33	As	2	2	6	2	6	10	2	3											
34	Se	2	2	6	2	6	10	2	4											
35	Br	2	2	6	2	6	10	2	5											
36	Kr	2	2	6	2	6	10	2	6											
37	Rb	2	2	6	2	6	10	2	6			1								
38	Sr	2	2	6	2	6	10	2	6			2								
39	Y	2	2	6	2	6	10	2	6	1		2								
40	Zr	2	2	6	2	6	10	2	6	2		2								
41	Nb	2	2	6	2	6	10	2	6	4		1								
42	Mo	2	2	6	2	6	10	2	6	5		1								
43	Tc	2	2	6	2	6	10	2	6	6		1								
44	Ru	2	2	6	2	6	10	2	6	7		1								
45	Rh	2	2	6	2	6	10	2	6	8		1								
46	Pd	2	2	6	2	6	10	2	6	10										
47	Ag	2	2	6	2	6	10	2	6	10		1								
48	Cd	2	2	6	2	6	10	2	6	10		2								
49	In	2	2	6	2	6	10	2	6	10		1	2							
50	Sn	2	2	6	2	6	10	2	6	10		2	2							
51	Sb	2	2	6	2	6	10	2	6	10		2	3							
52	Te	2	2	6	3	0	10	2	6	10		2	4							
53	I	2	2	6	2	6	10	2	6	10		2	5							

List of Elements Showing Grouping of Electrons in Shells

		K	L		M			N				O				P				Q
		1s	2s	2p	3s	3p	3d	4s	4p	4d	4f	5s	5p	5d	5f	6s	6p	6d	6f	7
54	Xe	2	2	6	2	6	10	2	6	10		2	6							
55	Cs	2	2	6	2	6	10	2	6	10		2	6			1				
56	Ba	2	2	6	2	6	10	2	6	10		2	6			2				
57	La	2	2	6	2	6	10	2	6	10		2	6	1		2				
58	Ce	2	2	6	2	6	10	2	6	10	2	2	6			2				
59	Pr	2	2	6	2	6	10	2	6	10	3	2	6			2				
60	Nd	2	2	6	2	6	10	2	6	10	4	2	6			2				
61	Pm	2	2	6	2	6	10	2	6	10	5	2	6			2				
62	Sm	2	2	6	2	6	10	2	6	10	6	2	6			2				
63	Eu	2	2	6	2	6	10	2	6	10	7	2	6			2				
64	Gd	2	2	6	2	6	10	2	6	10	7	2	6	1		2				
65	Tb	2	2	6	2	6	10	2	6	10	9	2	6			2				
66	Dy	2	2	6	2	6	10	2	6	10	10	2	6			2				
67	Ho	2	2	6	2	6	10	2	6	10	11	2	6			2				
68	Er	2	2	6	2	6	10	2	6	10	12	2	6			2				
69	Tm	2	2	6	2	6	10	2	6	10	13	2	6			2				
70	Yb	2	2	6	2	6	10	2	6	10	14	2	6			2				
71	Lu	2	2	6	2	6	10	2	6	10	14	2	6	1		2				
72	Hf	2	2	6	2	6	10	2	6	10	14	2	6	2		2				
73	Ta	2	2	6	2	6	10	2	6	10	14	2	6	3		2				
74	W	2	2	6	2	6	10	2	6	10	14	2	6	4		2				
75	Re	2	2	6	2	6	10	2	6	10	14	2	6	5		2				
76	Os	2	2	6	2	6	10	2	6	10	14	2	6	6		2				
77	Ir	2	2	6	2	6	10	2	6	10	14	2	6	7		2				
78	Pt	2	2	6	2	6	10	2	6	10	14	2	6	8		2				
79	Au	2	2	6	2	6	10	2	6	10	14	2	6	10		1				
80	Hg	2	2	6	2	6	10	2	6	10	14	2	6	10		2				
81	Tl	2	2	6	2	6	10	2	6	10	14	2	6	10		2	1			
82	Pb	2	2	6	2	6	10	2	6	10	14	2	6	10		2	2			
83	Bi	2	2	6	2	6	10	2	6	10	14	2	6	10		2	3			
84	Po	2	2	6	2	6	10	2	6	10	14	2	6	10		2	4			
85	At	2	2	6	2	6	10	2	6	10	14	2	6	10		2	5			
86	Rn	2	2	6	2	6	10	2	6	10	14	2	6	10		2	6			
87	Fa	2	2	6	2	6	10	2	6	10	14	2	6	10		2	6			
88	Ra	2	2	6	2	6	10	2	6	10	14	2	6	10		2	6			
89	Ac	2	2	6	2	6	10	2	6	10	14	2	6	10		2	6	1		
90	Th	2	2	6	2	6	10	2	6	10	14	2	6	10		2	6	2		
91	Pa	2	2	6	2	6	10	2	6	10	14	2	6	10	2	2	6	1		
92	U	2	2	6	2	6	10	2	6	10	14	2	6	10	3	2	6	1		
93	Np	2	2	6	2	6	10	2	6	10	14	2	6	10	4	2	6			
94	Pu	2	2	6	2	6	10	2	6	10	14	2	6	10	6	2	6			
95	Am	2	2	6	2	6	10	2	6	10	14	2	6	10	7	2	6	1		
96	Cm	2	2	6	2	6	10	2	6	10	14	2	6	10	8	2	6	1		
97	Bk	2	2	6	2	6	10	2	6	10	14	2	6	10	9	2	6			
98	Cf	2	2	6	2	6	10	2	6	10	14	2	6	10	10	2	6			
99	Es														11	2	6			
100	Fm														12	2	6			
101	Md														13	2	6			
102	No														14	2	6			

Bonds and Free Radicals

Ordinary chemical compounds are held together by bonds between the atoms. These bonds consist of pairs of electrons localized in the space between the atoms and lying closer to the more acidic atom. As a result the entire compound molecule has an even number of electrons. Sometimes, however, molecules exist with an odd number of electrons. The unpaired electron has a strong tendency to pair with any other electron it can find, and as a result such molecules, known as free radicals, are often very reactive. The odd electron also causes the molecule to be colored. An example is the brown gas nitrogen dioxide, NO_2, which pairs up its odd electron by reacting with itself to form a colorless gas consisting of the double molecule O_2NNO_2.

Neutrons in the Nucleus

The idea of electron shells outside the nucleus suggested that there may be similar "shells" of protons and neutrons inside the nucleus. The protons (or neutrons) in a given "shell" would have similar properties. This idea gained support with the recognition of certain "magic numbers" which signify numbers of neutrons and protons which result in extraordinary nuclear stability. Outside of the lightest elements, these magic numbers are 28, 50, 82, 126.

The Periodic Law

Excerpt from the following:
THE PERIODIC LAW *of the Chemical Elements. By Professor Mendeleeff.[1] (Faraday Lecture delivered before the Fellows of the Chemical Society in the Theatre of the Royal Institution, on Tuesday, June 4th, 1889).*

➔ THE HIGH honor bestowed by the Chemical Society in inviting me to pay a tribute to the world-famed name of Faraday by delivering this lecture has induced me to take for its subject the Periodic Law of the Elements—this being a generalization in chemistry which has of late attracted much attention. . . .

It was in March, 1869, that I ventured to lay before the then youthful Russian Chemical Society the ideas upon the same subject which I had expressed in my just written "Principles of Chemistry."

Without entering into details, I will give the conclusions I then arrived at, in the very words I used:

"1. The elements, if arranged according to their atomic weights, exhibit an evident *periodicity* of properties.

"Elements which are similar as regards their chemical properties have atomic weights which are either of nearly the same value (*e.g.*, platinum, iridium, osmium) or which increase regularly (*e.g.*, potassium, rubidium, cesium).

"3. The arrangement of the elements, or of groups of elements in the order of their atomic weights corresponds to their

[1] Mendeleeff is variously transliterated from Russian into English, a modern preferred form being Mendeleyev. It appeared as Mendeleeff in the Faraday Lectures.

so-called *valencies* as well as, to some extent, to their distinctive chemical properties—as is apparent among other series in that of lithium, beryllium, barium, carbon, nitrogen, oxygen and iron.

"4. The elements which are the most widely diffused have *small* atomic weights.

"5. The *magnitude* of the atomic weight determines the character of the element just as the magnitude of the molecule determines the character of a compound body.

"6. We must expect the discovery of many yet unknown elements, for example, elements analogous to aluminum and silicon, whose atomic weight would be between 65 and 75.

"7. The atomic weight of an element may sometimes be amended by a knowledge of the contiguous elements. . . .

"8. Certain characteristic properties of the elements can be foretold from their atomic weights.

Harmonic Periodicity

"The aim of this communication will be fully attained if I succeed in drawing the attention of investigators to those relations which exist between the atomic weights of dissimilar elements, which, as far as I know, have hitherto been almost completely neglected. I believe that the solution of some of the most important problems of our science lies in researches of this kind."

Today, 20 years after the above conclusions were formulated, they may still be considered as expressing the essence of the now well-known periodic law. . . .

The periodic law has shown that our chemical individuals display a harmonic periodicity of properties, dependent on their masses. Now, natural science has long been accustomed to deal with periodicities observed in nature, to seize them with the vise of mathematical analysis, to submit them to the rasp of experiment. And these instruments of scientific thought would surely, long since, have mastered the problem connected with the chemical elements, were it not for a new feature which was brought to light by the periodic law and which gave a peculiar and original character to the periodic function.

If we mark on an axis of abscissae a series of lengths proportional to angles, and trace ordinates which are proportional to sines or other trigonometrical functions, we get periodic curves of a harmonic character. So it might seem, at first sight, that with the increase of atomic weights the function of the properties of the elements should also vary in the same harmonious way. But in this case there is no such continuous change as in the curves just referred to, because the periods do not contain the infinite number of points constituting a curve, but a *finite* number only of such points. An example will better illustrate this view. The atomic weights—

Ag = 108, Cd =112, In = 113, Sn = 118, Sb = 120, Te

= 125, I = 127 steadily increase, and their increase is accompanied by a modification of many properties which constitutes the essence of the periodic law. Thus, for example, the densities of the above elements decrease steadily, being respectively—

10.5, 8.6, 7.4, 7.2, 6.7, 6.4, 4.9 while their oxides contain an increasing quantity of oxygen—

Ag_2O Cd_2O_2 In_2O_3, Sn_2O_4, Sb_2O_5, Te_2O_6, I_2O_7

But to connect by a curve the summits of the ordinates expressing any of these properties would involve a rejection of Dalton's law of multiple proportions. Not only are there no intermediate elements between silver, which gives $AgCl$, and cadmium, which gives $CdCl_2$, but, according to the very essence of the periodic law there can be none; in fact a uniform curve would be inapplicable in such a case, as it would lead us to expect elements possessed of special properties at any point of the curve. The periods of the elements have thus a character very different from those which are so simply represented by geometers. They correspond to points, to numbers, to sudden changes of the masses, and not to a continuous evolution. . . .

Elements Predicted

In the remaining part of my communication I shall endeavor to show, and as briefly as possible, in how far the periodic law contributes to enlarge our range of vision. Before the promulgation of this law the chemical elements were mere fragmentary, incidental facts in Nature; there was no special reason to expect the discovery of new elements, and the new ones which were discovered from time to time appeared to be possessed of quite novel properties. The law of periodicity first enabled us to perceive undiscovered elements at a distance which formerly was inaccessible to chemical vision; and long ere they were discovered new elements appeared before our eyes possessed of a number of well-defined properties. We now know three cases of elements whose existence and properties were foreseen by the instrumentality of the periodic law.

I need but mention the brilliant discovery of *gallium*, which proved to correspond to eka-aluminum of the periodic law, by Lecoq de Boisbaudran; of *scandium*, corresponding to eka-boron, by Nilson; and of *germanium*, which proved to correspond in all respects to eka-silicon, by Winckler. When, in 1871, I described to the Russian Chemical Society the properties, clearly defined by the periodic law, which such elements ought to possess, I never hoped that I should live to mention their discovery to the Chemical Society of Great Britain as a confirmation of the exactitude and the generality of the periodic law. Now, that I have had the happiness of doing so, I unhesitatingly say that although greatly enlarging our vision, even now the periodic law needs further improvements in order that it may become a trustworthy instrument in further discoveries.*

Abundance of the Elements

➤ WHETHER one takes a cosmical or an earthly view of atomic abundance will determine which elements are most plentiful.

In the crust of the earth which consists of igneous rocks, the most abundant element is oxygen, then silicon, then aluminum, then iron, followed by calcium, sodium, potassium, magnesium and titanium. These nine elements make up 99.25% of the earth's crust.

Hydrogen, with helium as a close second, is by far the most plentiful element taking into account the stars and the whole universe.

Two tables are reprinted from authoritative sources giving elemental abundances.

The table showing the average composition of igneous rocks, listing major and common elements by per cent by weight, is from the chapter in the *Internal Constitution of the Earth,* edited by G. Gutenberg (Dover, 1951) which gives revised figures for the famous relative abundance of the chemical elements that goes back to the work of F. W. Clarke, H. S. Washington, etc. as arranged by L. H. Adams. This shows the relationship of elements in the ground beneath our feet, which is what we have to use. (*Page 14*).

A universal view of atomic abundances of the elements is given by the table prepared by Harold C. Urey for his *The Planets, Their Origin and Development* (Yale, 1952). This question of how much there is of what in the universe is still far from settled, but Dr. Urey's figures are based upon the values of both V. M. Goldschmidt and Harrison S. Brown as well as his own calculations. In this table, the amounts of other elements are in terms of silicon being 10,000. (*Page 13*).

* I foresee some more new elements, but not with the same certitude as before. I shall give one example, and yet I do not see it quite distinctly. In the series which contains $Hg = 204$, $Pb = 206$ and $Bi = 208$, we can guess the existence of an element analogous to tellurium, which we can describe as dvi-tellurium Dt, having an atomic weight of 212, and the property of forming the oxide DtO_3. If this element really exists, it ought in the free state to be an easily fusible, crystalline, non-volatile metal of a grey color, having a density of about 9.3, capable of giving a dioxide. DtO_2, equally endowed with feeble acid and basic properties. This dioxide must give on active oxidation an unstable higher oxide, DtO_3, which should resemble in its properties PbO_2 and Bi_2O_5. Dvi-tellurium hydride, if it be found to exist, will be a less stable compound than even H_2Te. The compounds of dvi-tellurium will be easily reduced, and it will form characteristic definite alloys with other metals.

Atomic Abundances of the Elements
Silicon = 10,000

1. H	3.5×10^8		43. Tc	
2. He	3.5×10^7		44. Ru	0.019
3. Li	1.0		45. Rh	0.0067
4. Be	0.2		46. Pd	0.0091
5. B	0.24		47. Ag	0.023
6. C	80,000		48. Cd	0.055
7. N	160,000		49. In	0.0048
8. O	220,000		50. Sn	1.42
9. F	90		51. Sb	0.0097
10. Ne	9,000-240,000		52. Te	0.013
11. Na	462		53. I	0.014
12. Mg	8,870		54. Xe	
13. Al	882		55. Cs	0.001
14. Si	10,000		56. Ba	0.039
15. P	90		57. La	0.021
16. S	1,800		58. Ce	0.023
17. Cl	170		59. Pr	0.0096
18. A	130-2,200		60. Nd	0.033
19. K	69		61. Pm	
20. Ca	660		62. Sm	0.012
21. Sc	0.18		63. Eu	0.0028
22. Ti	27		64. Gd	0.017
23. V	2.4		65. Tb	0.0052
24. Cr	93		66. Dy	0.020
25. Mn	75		67. Ho	0.0057
26. Fe	7,250		68. Er	0.016
27. Co	22		69. Tm	0.0029
28. Ni	300		70. Yb	0.015
29. Cu	7.1		71. Lu	0.0048
30. Zn	2.6		72. Hf	0.007
31. Ga	0.11		73. Ta	0.0029
32. Ge	1.4		74. W	0.14
33. As	2.3		75. Re	0.00066
34. Se	0.35		76. Os	0.011
35. Br	0.43		77. Ir	0.0025
36. Kr			78. Pt	0.016
37. Rb	0.071		79. Au	0.0015
38. Sr	0.41		80. Hg	0.00016
39. Y	0.10		81. Tl	0.0011
40. Zr	1.5		82. Pb	<0.02
41. Cb	0.0077		83. Bi	0.0013
42. Mo	0.072		90. Th	0.0012
			92. U	0.0002

Average Composition of Igneous Rocks, Per Cent by Weight

O	46.59	F	0.030
Si	27.72	Zr	0.026
Al	8.13	Ni	0.020
Fe	5.01	Sr	0.019
Ca	3.63	V	0.017
Na	2.85	Ce,Y	0.015
K	2.60	Cu	0.010
Mg	2.09	U	0.008
Ti	0.63	W	0.005
P	0.13	Li	0.004
H	0.13	Zn	0.004
Mn	0.10	Cb,Ta	0.003
S	0.052	Hf	0.003
Ba	0.050	Th	0.002
Cl	0.048	Pb	0.002
Cr	0.037	Co	0.001
C	0.032	B	0.001
		Be	0.001

Useful Materials

Excerpt from Resources for Freedom, *Vol. IV: The Promise of Technology, U. S. Govt. Printing Office, Washington, D. C., 1952.*

→Our materials and energy resources may be divided into two major categories: (*a*) those that we use on a large scale as the basic production ingredients of our economy and (*b*) those that we presently use very little or not at all. These two categories may be further subdivided into materials which are plentiful when we compare the rate of use with known reserves and those which are scarce by the same criterion. Each of these four categories has its technological problems, which differ in kind and importance.

Present Materials

The abundant materials we now use on a huge scale include iron, aluminum, coal (both as a source of energy and as a raw material); materials, such as sulfur and salt, for making basic chemicals (i.e., sulfuric acid, chlorine, caustic soda, and soda ash); and the nonmetallic building materials. Because of the large-scale use and basic importance of these materials, slight increases in cost can have tremendous effects on the whole economy of the country. Therefore, technology has the task of holding costs down.

Ample resources of varying concentrations exist for all of

these materials. For this reason discovery techniques, while important, are not the chief problem. If rich iron ores are no longer available, we know where other ores are, and we can use a lower grade ore at a tolerable cost. If sulfur deposits suitable for the Frasch process can no longer be found at a sufficient rate, we can use volcanic sulfur, pyrites, pyrrhotite, or even gypsum. With this group as a whole the chief concern is to develop techniques for processing lower grade resources without permitting costs to throttle development.

The resources that are plentiful in relation to their use include:

Coal and lignite
Iron ore
Sulfur and pyrites (sulfuric acid)
Salt (chlorine, caustic soda, etc.)
Bauxite (aluminum)
Potash
Phosphates
Air (oxygen, nitrogen, etc.)
Boron compounds
Water
Clay
Stone
Sand
Gypsum
Limestone
Bromine
Iodine

When we come to the scarce production materials we find ourselves dealing chiefly with metals and their ores, particularly the materials needed for making steel and its alloys—manganese, nickel, chromium, molybdenum, tungsten, vanadium, and cobalt. Fluorspar, the hydrocarbons, petroleum, and natural gas, and forest resources also fall into this category. These are our problem materials.

In this classification the main problem is availability and cost, though vital, is secondary. These substances we presently cannot do without, and their supply is limited. In each case the question is whether the material is irreplaceable in the particular uses to which it is put, or whether some more plentiful material can give the same service. We must also make sure that mining and processing operations do not unnecessarily disperse some of the material which is being extracted. We must find further ways of recovering and recycling dispersed material so that the total of new material required will be reduced. With this group especially we must find ways of discovering new sources of supply. In the case of our forest resources we must try to increase their rate of renewability as well as decrease unnecessary dispersion.

The resources that are scarce in relation to their use include:

COMMON METALS:
Copper
Lead
Zinc
Tin

UNCOMMON METALS:
Mercury
Cadmium
Selenium
Cerium
Antimony
Bismuth
Noble Metals (gold, etc.)
Radioactive Metals
Germanium
Beryllium
Platinum Group

ADDITIVE METALS:
Manganese
Chromium
Nickel
Molybdenum
Tungsten
Tantalum
Vanadium
Cobalt
Columbium

OTHER MATERIALS:
Fluorspar
Petroleum
Natural Gas
Forest Products

Potential Materials

Some materials are abundant in nature but, compared to that abundance, little used. The problem with these materials is essentially one of learning how to produce and to use them in larger quantities and at lower cost. These are the materials from which substitutes for our problem materials could come. How can we produce titanium and where can we best use it? Can we make it cheaply enough so that it can be widely used as a substitute for scarce metals? What can we do to make silicon useful as a metal? How else can we use it? Can we expand its use in silicones as substitutes for scarce materials?

We know how to make magnesium. Can we overcome its defects in fabrication and use?

The plentiful resources include:

ALKALINE EARTH METALS:
  Magnesium
  Calcium

ALKALI METALS:
  Sodium
  Potassium

OTHER METALS:
  Titanium
  Zirconium
  Silicon Metal
  Polymeric Materials

Finally, there are materials both scarce and undeveloped. These include tellurium, rhenium, lithium, strontium, the rare earths, and others. Here the main job is to study every property of these elements and use them as far as possible only where they are essential.

The scarce resources include:
  Lithium
  Cesium
  Strontium
  Gallium
  Indium
  Hafnium
  Thallium
  Tellurium
  Rhenium
  Rare Earths

The Dominant Materials

The dominant materials today are those which support our whole economy and are at the same time abundant in relation to our needs.

In the case of the potash, phosphates, and fixed nitrogen group, the problems are relatively minor. Potash reserves are ample for several hundred years to come, and techniques are known which would at slightly higher cost increase reserves enormously from sources such as alunite, feldspar, leucite, etc. In addition, a process recently developed in Norway indicates that potash may be extracted from sea water by the use of specially prepared ion-exchange resins.

The situation with regard to phosphate rock is similar. There are large economic reserves and, in addition, practically inexhaustible quantities of low-grade material. A very large percentage of the nitrogen utilized by plant life is fixed by microorganisms in the soil. This nitrogen has been supplemented from other sources.

The Alkali Metals

Group Ia

ELEMENT   ELECTRON SHELLS

$$_1H = K_1$$
$$_3Li = K_2L_1$$
$$_{11}Na = K_2L_8M_1$$
$$_{19}K = K_2L_8M_8N_1$$
$$_{37}Rb = K_2L_8M_{18}N_8O_1$$
$$_{55}Cs = K_2L_8M_{18}N_{18}O_8P_1$$
$$_{87}Fa = K_2L_8M_{18}N_{32}O_{18}P_8Q_1$$

➤ IN COMPARING one element with another, many properties are considered. The resemblances which place an element in its proper group in the Periodic Table have to do with chemical combination rather than appearance, The inclusion of hydrogen, the gas whose presence often gives its compounds the quality of acidity, among the alkali metals is only one of the minor inconsistencies of that classification scheme.

The fact that in compounds with some metals, hydrogen forms the negative part of the molecule shows its double nature. Some authorities even classify hydrogen as a Group VII element as well as in Group I.

The valence, or combining power, of one, however, fits hydrogen in with many of the chemical characteristics of Group Ia elements.

The hydrogen atom has one electron with which to form compounds. Each of the metals which follow it in Group Ia has one electron in a new shell outside a "closed" shell of maximum stability.

This is shown in the accompanying table of the atomic structures of this group of elements. The inner or K shell, which holds two electrons when filled, begins with hydrogen. It is completed with helium, atomic number 2. With lithium, number 3, the L shell starts.

Sodium has the K and L shells complete, with 2 and 8 electrons respectively, and the M shell starting. Potassium has complete K and L shells and a stable configuration of 8 electrons in the M shell. Although only the first two subshells are filled by these 8 electrons, and a third subshell will eventually be added in heavier elements, in potassium the 19th electron starts a new outer shell, designated N.

Rubidium finds the M shell with its complement of 18 electrons, a stable configuration of 8 in shell N and in the O shell the single electron characteristic of Group Ia elements.

In cesium both the M and N shells have 18 electrons each. The M shell has its full complement, but the N shell can add another subshell, as is evident in the case of the next element, the newly-discovered francium. Cesium has one outer electron starting the P shell and francium's one starts the Q shell.

The naming of these shells is arbitrary. The structures of the elements are believed to be pictured with accuracy by this scheme of electron shells, and the chemical properties of the elements are believed to depend on the way electrons in some of the outer shells of the atoms can be detached, recaptured, or shared with other atoms.

Atoms whose outer (or valence) electrons have become detached are said to be *ionized*. Compounds formed by sharing pairs of electrons are said to be *covalent*.

Hydrogen

➤HYDROGEN is the lightest chemical element. Its mass is the unit of measurement for the masses of other elements.

Atomic weight, or mass, was long considered the most important property of an element. By weighing the amounts of individual elements making up a chemical compound and calculating the weights of these ratios to the weight of hydrogen which will combine with the same elements, the atomic weights of the other elements are found to be almost, but not quite, whole numbers.

During the nineteenth century a committee of chemists was chosen to decide upon standards of accuracy for atomic weights. That committee set the atomic weight of oxygen at 16.000, in order to make the atomic weights of other elements come out closer to whole numbers. That change of standards gave hydrogen the weight 1.008.

Hydrogen is given off by some natural gas wells, but it escapes into the upper air. It is not found uncombined on earth. It is recognized in the stars by its spectrum lines in the light we receive from them.

In combination with oxygen, in the form of water, and with carbon, in the many organic compounds, hydrogen is one of the most abundant elements on earth.

Hydrogen combines with other elements to form different kinds of compounds, some which ionize on solution, others which are joined with covalent bonds, yielding organic types of compounds.

Although usually classed with the alkali metals of Group I

in the Periodic Table, hydrogen acts as the negative part of the molecule when in combination with these metals. It forms hydrides which are in general colorless crystals. Similar compounds are formed with calcium and barium of Group II. The hydrides decompose in water, releasing hydrogen. This property has been used as a convenient way to store hydrogen. Lithium hydride was used for this purpose during World War II, in emergency radio sets to be used at sea. The lithium hydride when mixed with sea water evolves hydrogen to inflate small balloons which hold the end of the antenna wire aloft.

Hydrides of metals other than those of Groups I and II tend to be more stable, but to have properties more like those of metals instead of like salts. Niobium hydride (NbH) and germanium monohydride (GeH) are of this form.

Germane (GeH_4), on the other hand, forms a gaseous compound which is similar to methane (CH_4), borane (BH_4), silane (SiH_4), and stannane (SnH_4). The last in this list, with its greater molecular weight, is a liquid.

Methane is the starting point of a wide variety of compounds which carbon can form by joining atoms carbon-to-carbon together in the form of chains and rings. Single, double and triple bonds can unite carbon atoms one to another. Many other elements do not have this ability to unite atoms of the same species. Some of these, however, can form chains and links by alternating another kind of element between. Silicon and oxygen can alternate in this way to form chains of indefinite length-Si-O-Si-O.

Boron and nitrogen can alternate to form a ring compound which has many properties similar to the carbon benzene ring. Hydrogen atoms attach themselves to the chain- or ring-forming elements in these compounds in a way similar to the carbon compounds. Typical organic groups, such as CH_3-C_2H_5-, etc., can also join these other organic-type compounds, in many instances.

Hydrogen joins the halogen group of elements to form acids, which are ionized compounds. The proportion of hydrogen ions in such a solution is the measure of the acidity of the solution.

Other acids measured by their pH value are those formed by such complex radicals as HNO_3 H_2SO_4, etc.

Hydrogen is usually obtained by action of sulfuric acid (H_2SO_4) on zinc. The metal replaces the hydrogen, which bubbles off as a gas. Electrolysis of water also liberates hydrogen, at the cathode, while oxygen comes off at the anode.

Hydrogen was first obtained in 1766 by Sir Henry Cavendish in London. His account of his discovery is published in the Transactions of the Royal Society, Vol. 56. He found that he could get the gas by dissolving zinc, iron or tin in diluted vitriolic acid (H_2SO_4) or spirit of salt (HCl). He discovered that a mixture of hydrogen and common air explodes with a loud noise, and he was impressed with the lightness of the gas. He named the gas "inflammable air." The name *hydrogen* (water-former) was given by Lavoisier.

Hydrogen exists in three isotopic forms, known as hydrogen (or protium), deuterium and tritium. Tritium is radioactive, with a short half-life. Deuterium is stable, and occurs in a small amount with ordinary hydrogen. Its compound D_2O is known as heavy water. Slight differences between the properties of ordinary water and heavy water allow their separation, notably by electrolysis, in which ordinary water is decomposed and heavy water becomes concentrated in the water left in the apparatus.

The nuclear structure of ordinary hydrogen consists of one proton, the unit of matter. This is the same as a hydrogen ion. An electron as the sole planet in this system completes the structure of the hydrogen atom.

The difference between ordinary hydrogen and heavy hydrogen (deuterium) lies in the fact that deuterium has a neutron in the nucleus in addition to the proton. Addition of the neutron adds weight but does not change the chemical characteristics. This is in accordance with a general rule covering structures of elements.

Tritium has a nucleus consisting of one proton and two neutrons.

Physicists sometimes use the terms "ortho" and "para" hydrogen. In ortho hydrogen, nucleus and electron both spin on their axes in the same direction (as though from "west" to "east"). At ordinary temperatures 75% of any sample of hydrogen is ortho. As temperatures fall toward absolute zero, the spin of the particles changes to the para type, until nearly all electrons spin in the direction opposite to that of the nucleus.

Lithium

➤LITHIUM is the lightest metal among the elements, and the lightest element, aside from hydrogen, in Group I of the Periodic Table, the Alkali Metals. Like all the alkalies, its hydroxide is a strong base, and forms crystalline salts with acids. Lithium hydroxide will take up carbon dioxide from the atmosphere, and can be used as an air purifier. It forms Li_2CO_3. The metal is too active in forming compounds to make the use of metallic lithium practical, even in alloys. Lithium hydride has been mentioned above as a method of transporting hydrogen. Lithium oxide can be used in ceramics. The chloride and fluoride are used in welding fluxes, especially for aluminum.

Organic compounds containing lithium can be made and

lithium greases for low temperature lubrication are in commercial production.

Although a rare element, concentrations of lithium compounds are found in certain localities. *Spodumene,* a lithium-aluminum silicate, is found in North Carolina and two phosphates, *triphylite* and *lithiophilite,* occur in New England. Lithia springs used to be thought to have water of valuable medicinal qualities, but recent attempts to substitute lithium chloride for sodium chloride in the diet have been found to be dangerous, as the body cannot use the lithium ion.

Lithium was discovered in 1818 by August Arfwedson.[1] The account of the discovery was published in *Annales de Chimie et de Physique,* Vol. X, Paris, 1819.

Arfwedson was analyzing a rare mineral, *Pétalite,* from a mine at Utò in Sweden. He had found that it contained silica, alumina and sulfates. His report continues:

"But it was still necessary to learn the base of the salt. Its solution could not be precipitated either by tartaric acid in excess or by platinum chloride. Consequently it could not be potassium. I mixed another portion of a solution of the same salt with a few drops of pure potash, but without its becoming cloudy. Therefore, it contained no more magnesia: hence it must be a salt with soda for a base. I calculated the quantity of soda which would be necessary to form it; but it always resulted in an excess of about 5 parts in 100 of the mineral analyzed. . . .

"At last, having studied more closely the sulfate in question, I soon found that it contained a definite fixed alkali, whose nature had not previously been known. M. Berzelius proposed to give it the name of *lithion* (from the Greek word *lithios, stone*), because this alkali is the first found in the mineral kingdom."

Lithium, along with the other alkalies, belongs to the class of metals which forms mostly compounds soluble in water. Its most distinctive test is the red color its salts give to the Bunsen flame.

The atomic weight of lithium 6.94, results from the mixture of two stable isotopes, Li 7 which makes up about 93% of the normally occurring element and Li 6 which accounts for the rest. There is a radioactive isotope, Li 8, of very short life.

Sodium and Potassium

→ SODIUM and potassium were both known as alkalies extracted from the ashes of plants or from mineral deposits of

[1] The name of the author appears on this article spelled in this way. It is also spelled Arfvedson. Both spellings may be considered correct.

sea salt from earliest times. They were distinguished gradually, by the difference in their crystal forms. Sodium carbonate finally became known as the mineral alkali while the potassium compound, derived usually from wood ashes, took the name of the vegetable alkali.

Sir Humphry Davy, who investigated the electrolysis of salt solutions with the newly discovered electric battery, showed that such substances are compounds of metals. He obtained both sodium and potassium.

These discoveries were reported in the Bakerian Lecture, 1807: "On some new Phenomena of chemical changes produced by electricity, particularly the decomposition of the fixed alkalies, and the exhibition of the new substances which constitute their bases; and on the general nature of alkaline bodies."

Sir Humphry described his experiments: "A small piece of pure potash, which had been exposed for a few seconds to the atmosphere, so as to give conducting power to the surface, was placed upon an insulated disc of platina, connected with the negative side of the battery of the power of 250 of 6 and 4, in a state of intense activity; and a platina wire, communicating with the positive side, was brought in contact with the upper surface of the alkali. The whole apparatus was in the open atmosphere.

"Under these circumstances a vivid action was soon observed to take place. The potash began to fuse at both its points of electrization. There was a violent effervescence at the upper surface; at the lower, or negative surface, there was no liberation of elastic fluid; but small globules having a high metallic lustre, and being precisely similar in visible characters to quicksilver, appeared, some of which burnt with explosion and bright flame, as soon as they were formed, and others remained, and were merely tarnished, and finally covered by a white film which formed on their surfaces.

"These globules, numerous experiments soon shewed to be the substance I was in search of, and a peculiar inflammable principle the basis of potash. I found that the platina was in no way connected with the result, except as the medium for exhibiting the electrical powers of decomposition; and a substance of the same kind was produced when pieces of copper, silver, gold, plumbago, or even charcoal were employed for compleating the circuit. . . .

"Soda, when acted upon in the same manner as potash, exhibited an analogous result; but the decomposition demanded greater intensity of action in the batteries, or the alkali was required to be in much thinner and smaller pieces. . . .

"The substance produced from potash remained fluid at the temperature of the atmosphere at the time of its production; that from soda, which was fluid in the degree of heat of the alkali during its formation, became solid on cooling, and appeared having the lustre of silver."

Rubidium and Cesium

→ RUBIDIUM and cesium, as heavier elements of the alkali metals group, are even more active and more basic in their combinations than sodium and potassium.

As somewhat rare elements for which few especial uses have been found, the interest in these two elements lies largely in the way they were discovered.

Chemical News, London, for Nov. 24, 1860, carried this announcement: "In a recent number of the *Philosophical Magazine* there is given an account of some researches by MM. Bunsen and Kirchhoff on the effect produced by various metals on the spectrum of a flame in which their chlorides are volatilized. That part of their investigation which is more particularly interesting consists of a method of photochemical analysis of exquisite delicacy, which the authors have especially studied in relation to the alkali-metals.

"These metals have been employed in the form of chlorides which have been purified with the greatest care. When these are introduced into a jet of flame they volatilize to a greater or less extent, and then communicate to the flame the special character above alluded to, and which is observable when the spectrum produced by the flame is examined by a sufficient magnifying power.

"The above-named memoir is accompanied by a colored plate which illustrates the spectra of the alkali-metals with their characteristic rays. These rays are the more visible in proportion as the flame is less luminous and its temperature higher. The ordinary Bunsen gas-burner answers admirably for these experiments. The rays shown by the chlorides of potassium, sodium, and lithium are perfectly well-defined; those of barium, strontium, and calcium are more complicated, and require a somewhat experienced eye for their identification. They are, however, quite distinct enough to be easily recognized, even when the salts of these metals are mixed together; for the great advantage of this method of analysis is, that foreign matters have no influence on the results, the authors being able to detect with certainty the different elements in a mixture containing the tenth of a milligramme of the metals mentioned above. Sodium, with its yellow ray, first appears; after that the well-defined red ray of lithium; next is seen the paler rays indicating potassium; and, after these rays have disappeared, they are replaced by those of calcium and strontium, which remain visible for some time. The absence

Starting with a salt of actinium-carrying lanthanum carefully purified of its derivatives, we eliminated the last traces of radio-actinium by precipitation with cerium hydroxide in an oxidizing medium, and of the active deposit by precipitation with hydrogen sulfide in the presence of lead; we then precipitated the actinium-carrying lanthanum, in the presence of barium, with decarbonated ammonia, which leaves the actinium X in solution.

During the first two hours following the end of the purification, we found that the beta ray activity increases at first with a period of about 20 minutes, forming a plateau next, then increasing on account of the formation of derivatives.

We thought that this initial increase in activity might perhaps be due to the formation of an active deposit due to traces of actinium X which had not been eliminated. So we tried, but in vain, to remove this activity by precipitation with lead sulfide.

This original appearance had never before been reported; it thus seemed logical to attribute its formation in actinium to a new radioelement separated in the course of the purification. The beta ray of this substance is absorbed by as little as 18/100 mm. of aluminum ($w=39$ cm^{-1}). Measured as beta rays, the value of the plateau represents about $\frac{1}{2}$ per 100 of the activity of the product at equilibrium.

To characterize the chemical identity of this new *naturally* radioactive body, we tried to determine at what moment of the operation it is separated from actinium. The mother liquor of the last purification, which in consequence of the precipitations ought to be inactive and ought to contain only ammoniacal salts, when evaporated to dryness showed a beta activity which decayed with the same period of 21 minutes as the preceding. In repeated precipitations with cerium hydroxide, with lead sulfide and with barium carbonate, this activity was not carried down, which seems to mean an alkaline element.

According to the hypothesis that this radioelement is formed by emission of alpha particles given off from actinium, it would occupy place 87 in the periodic table; to prove this we have tried to establish the chemical analogy of this substance with cesium by crystallization with it. Cesium perchlorate was chosen for this purpose, by reason of the slight solubility which distinguishes it from the very soluble perchlorates of non-alkaline metals. Upon adding cesium chloride to the mother liquor and precipitating it with a solution of sodium perchlorate, crystals are formed which carry the activity. This decays exponentially with a period of 21 ± 1 min.

This is characteristic of the heavier homologue of cesium, of atomic number 87.

Its formation by disintegration of actinium can be understood only by emission of an alpha particle. This is why we found such a ray in the residue of actinium freed from its derivatives. We have actually observed an alpha ray of 3.5 cm. free path in the air, T.P.N., a ray which has been found[1] and, later, attributed to traces of protactinium.[2]. We made sure that our product was free from protactinium originally; on the other hand, if there were any traces in it, the precipitation of radioactinium with cerium hydroxide would eliminate them.

We are thus led to believe that this *naturally radioactive* element, of 21 minutes period, with atomic number 87, is derived, by alpha ray disintegration, from actinium. It must be that actinium has a weak branch alpha, as though a mixture of two isotopes is disintegrating, one by beta ray, the other by alpha.

New Elements Named

The discovery of element 87 by Mlle. Perey came at the time when atomic transformations were about to become better understood.

Earlier, when the disintegration products of radium were the only ones well known, the successive products were identified chiefly by the rays they give off. It was natural to name them radium A, radium B, etc., from their source.

As disintegration products of other elements came to be known, these formed other series of products similarly named. Mlle. Perey followed this pattern in naming her new radioactive material Actinium K as the next actinium product in order of discovery. No account is taken, in this scheme, of the chemical properties of these disintegration products.

In the course of time, as certain products of separate disintegration series became recognized as isotopes of the same element, the name of that element came to be used instead of the older nomenclature. Atomic transmutation, so long synonymous with the impossible, thus gradually became accepted as fact.

In 1946, Prof. F. A. Paneth, of the University of Durham, called attention to the fact that discovery of elements 43, 61, 85 and 87 had been proved but that the discoverers had not given chemical names to these substances.

One reason for this omission was that chemists were at one time reluctant to admit that a radioactive isotope is as genuine an elemental form as a stable one.

"The denial of full citizenship to artificial elements seemed justified in those days," said Dr. Paneth. "They had been produced in invisible amount only, and they were unstable and usually not present on earth; whereas in the case of all

[1] St. Meyer, V. F. Hess et F. Paneth, *Wiener Ber.* 123: 1914, p. 1459.
[2] Meyer-Schweidler, *Radioaktivität*, 1927, p. 471.

the natural elements, we could be sure that, even if they belonged to the radioactive families and were only represented by fairly short-lived isotopes, very considerable quantities always existed. (For example, the laws of radioactive equilibrium ensure the presence in the upper 60 km. of the earth's crust of more than 10,000 tons of polonium). The limited importance attributed until a few years ago to the artificially produced elements was reflected also by the absence of names suggested for them. . . .

"Today the situation is very different. . . . The availability of any desired quantity of element 94 opens the way to the production of visible amounts of elements still higher in the Periodic System. Finally, the uranium pile has given us the means of creating lighter elements in bulk too; among the very products of uranium fission are many new isotopes not only of well-known elements, but also of the missing elements 43 and 61, which can thus be obtained in a far greater quantity than by any previous method. The chemistry of some of the newly created elements is already known as well as, or better than, that of some of the less important ones which were discovered in Nature many decades ago, and their practical application is at least a possibility."

As a result of Paneth's instigation, the British journal *Nature*, in the issue of Jan. 4, 1947, carried letters from Perrier and E. Segre naming No. 43 "Technetium", and from D. R. Corson, K. R. Mackenzie and E. Segre naming No. 85 "Astatine." There was also the statement from Paneth that Mlle. Perey wished to call No. 87 "Francium".

Shortly thereafter J. A. Marinsky, L. E. Glendenin and C. D. Coryell announced "Promethium" as the name for No. 61. Earlier names (43 Masurium, 85 Alabamine, 87 Virginium, 61 Illinium) which had been proposed for the elements expected for those places were then dropped.

The Alkaline Earths

Group IIα

ELEMENT   ELECTRON SHELLS

$_4Be = K_2L_2$

$_{12}Mg = K_2L_8M_2$

$_{20}Ca = K_2L_8M_8N_2$

$_{38}Sr = K_2L_8M_{18}N_8O_2$

$_{56}Ba = K_2L_8M_{18}N_{18}O_8P_2$

$_{88}Ra = K_2L_8M_{18}N_{32}O_{18}P_8Q_2$

➤First known in the form of their oxides, whose texture is like that of earth, the alkaline earths were well known long before they were analyzed. The presence of metal in the compounds of these elements came as a surprise. Discovery of radium was probably the greatest surprise in chemical history.

As a group they have similar properties. As usual, the lightest member of the set is least like the others in its compounds. Stable oxides and carbonates, hydroxides less caustic than those of Group I, and the appearance of some insoluble compounds characterize the alkaline earth elements. The typical valence is two. This is due to the two electrons in the outer shell of each element in this group.

Spectra are more complicated than those of Group I elements, but well marked. The Bunsen flame is colored red by salts of strontium and radium, as it is by lithium in Group I. Barium gives a fleeting yellow-green color which can be intensified by mixing the salt with alcohol.

Beryllium

Excerpt from the following:
ANALYSIS OF THE AQUAMARINE OR BERYL; *and the Discovery of a New Earth in That Stone. Read before the French National Institute, 26 Pluvoise, in the Year VI. (Feb. 14, 1798.) By Citizen Vauquelin. In Nicholson's Journal of Natural Philosophy, Chemistry, and the Arts, Vol. II., London, M.DCC.-XCIX (1799).*
➤THE ANALYSIS of minerals is one of those operations which

are usually considered to be of little importance and are submitted, by chemists of the first order, as unworthy of their care, to the manipulation of their pupils.

I am well aware that the greater number of analyses afford results of little importance, which do not repay the labour and the time bestowed in obtaining them. I am likewise aware that they do not offer so brilliant a prospect, nor promise to afford results of so general a nature, as the plan of operation which has been formed with regard to some of the most important points in chemistry. But I am not, from these reasons, of opinion, that this class of processes, which has likewise its difficulties, and requires, for its successful conduct, a certain series of reasoning and particularly an exact knowledge of the bodies described; I am not of opinion that it is so little entitled to engage the attention of philosophical chemists. For they must recollect, that it has afforded them the solid foundation of their theories, and new objects for the exercise of their abilities.

From a disregard of this kind it was that Bergman, whose active mind could not submit to the details of experiment, has committed so many faults, by trusting his operations to young pupils, who had not acquired the habit of distinguishing new substances from those which were already known.

The analysis of the beryl, already made by Bindheim, will be a proof of what I here advance. It is composed, according to him, of silex 64, alumine 27, lime 8, and iron 2.

Citizen Haüy having found a perfect agreement between the structure, hardness and weight of the beryl and the emerald, engaged me, some months ago, to compare these two stones by chemical means also, in order to know whether they were composed of the same principles in similar proportions.

The most interesting circumstance to the Institute in this result being a new earth, which I have discovered in the beryl, I shall pass slightly over the other subjects, and dwell more particularly on its distinctive properties.

The Method of Analysis

Experiment 1. One hundred parts of beryl reduced to fine powder were fused with 300 parts of caustic potash; the mass, after cooling, was diffused in water, and treated with the muriatic acid; by this means the solution was completed.

The muriatic solution was evaporated to dryness; toward the end of the evaporation the fluid assumed the form of a jelly; the dried matter was then diffused in a large quantity of water. Part of the matter was dissolved; but a white, granulated transparent powder remained. This substance, collected on a filter, washed with much water, and dried by ignition, weighed 69 parts. It had all the properties of silex.

Experiment 2. The fluid separated from the silex was precipitated by the carbonate of potash of commerce; the precipitate collected and drained was treated with a solution of caustic potash. The greatest part of the matter was dissolved; but there remained a certain quantity of earth which was not taken up. This being separated, washed, and dried by ignition, was of a brown greyish colour; it weighed nine parts. In these nine parts it is that our new earth is contained. We shall speak of it again in the subsequent part of this Memoir.

Experiment 3. The alkaline solution of the foregoing experiment was supersaturated with muriatic acid, until a perfect solution took place, and this was again precipitated by the carbonate of the potash of commerce: the deposition, washed and dried by a red heat, weighed 21 parts.

This substance appeared to me at that time to be pure alumine. We shall see what conclusion ought to be made, after examining the properties of the new earth which I have announced.

Experiment 4. The nine parts in *Experiment 2* remaining after the action of the potash, and in which I announced the existence of a new earth, were dissolved in the nitric acid; the solution was evaporated to dryness, and the residue again dissolved in water. The solution of this substance having assumed a reddish yellow colour, which indicated the presence of iron, a solution of the hydro-sulphuret of potash was mixed with it; a black voluminous precipitate was formed; the fluid was heated in order to favour the union of the parts, after which the fluid was decanted clear and colourless. The black precipitate by calcination became of a red brown colour, and weighed one part. When dissolved in the muriatic acid, and the solution evaporated to dryness, it afforded a beautiful blue when an atom of the matter was thrown into a solution of the Prussiate of potash: it was therefore the oxide of iron.

Experiment 5. The earth being thus perfectly deprived of the oxide of iron, I separated it from the nitric acid by means of the common carbonate of potash; and I obtained 12 parts of a white earth, soft beneath the fingers, and soluble in acids with effervescence.

We see that this earth, in its separation from the nitric acid, did absorb four parts and a half of carbonic acid; since out of nine which were subjected to experiment, one and a half of the oxide of iron were obtained; which leaves 7.5 for the earth contained in the 12 parts of carbonate last precipitated.

Comparison with Alumine

Experiment 1. For this purpose. I separately dissolved equal quantities of alumine and of the earth of beryl in nitric acid, to perfect saturation.

The salt which arose from the combination of the earth of beryl with the nitric acid, did not appear susceptible of crystallization; it strongly retains moisture; by dessication it becomes converted into a kind of ductile paste, which, when exposed to the air, powerfully attracts moisture. Its taste is at first very sweet, and afterwards astringent.

Experiment 2. The nitrate of alumine likewise crystallizes with considerable difficulty; but it does not attract moisture so strongly. Its taste is not saccharine, like that of the nitrate formed with the earth of beryl.

I made the following comparative essays of the solution of these two salts, using equal quantities of each.

1. The nitrate of alumine, mixed with a solution of nut-galls in alcohol, afforded no precipitate. The fluid simply acquired a slight greenish colour, and lost somewhat of its transparence; however, at the expiration of some hours, the fluid, having been diluted with water, let fall a greyish precipitate.—2. The salt of the earth of beryl, mixed with the same re-agent, immediately afforded a deposition in flocks of a yellow brown colour.

3. The nitrate of alumine, mixed with the oxalate of potash, immediately afforded a precipitate in the form of very abundant white flocks, which subsided to the lower part of the vessel, and left the superior fluid perfectly clear.—4. The salt of the earth of beryl, with the same re-agent, did not afford the slightest appearance of a precipitate, even after several days.

5. The nitrate of alumine, mixed with tartrite of potash, immediately formed a deposition in flocks, and the supernatant liquor became clear and colourless.—6. The salt of the earth of beryl, with the same re-agent, did not produce any sign of precipitation after several days.

7. The nitrate of alumine, mixed with a solution of the phosphate of soda, afforded a gelatinous semi-transparent precipitate, which subsided very slowly.—8. The salt of the earth of beryl also formed a precipitate with the same re-agent; but it was less gelatinous, and less transparent, and it also fell down more speedily.

9. The nitrate of alumine, mixed with very pure Prussiate of potash, instantly afforded a very abundant whitish precipitate, which became green at the end of a few hours.—10. The salt of the earth of beryl, with the same re-agent, afforded no precipitate even after several days.

11. The nitrate of alumine, mixed with a saturated solution of potash, afforded a gelatinous magma, which was semi-transparent, and soon became filled with numerous bubbles of gas, which raised it to the upper part of the fluid.—12. The salt of the earth of beryl, mixed with the same re-agent, afforded a precipitate in flocks, which was not filled with bubbles like the foregoing, and which fell to the bottom of the liquid.

13. The nitrate of alumine, mixed with a solution of caustic potash, at first afforded a gelatinous deposition, which was afterwards taken up by the excess of alkali.—14. The salt of

the earth of beryl, treated with the same re-agent, was affected in the same manner, excepting only that a larger quantity of alkali was required for the second solution.

15. The nitrate of alumine, mixed with a solution of carbonate of ammonia, formed a precipitate which was not re-dissolved by an excess of alkali.—16. The salt of the earth of beryl, mixed with the same re-agent, afforded a precipitate which was entirely re-dissolved by an excess of alkali.

We see by most of these experiments, that the earth of beryl essentially differs from alumine, which however it resembles much more than any other earth, and with which it may even be easily confounded in certain respects.

Earth of Beryl

Now it is evident that the earth of beryl has more affinity with the nitric acid than alumine has, and consequently that it is not the same earth. If the earth of beryl be not alumine, there is much greater reason to decide, that it is not one of the other known earths; for it differs much more from them than from alumine. I therefore consider this earth as a new substance, different from all those we are yet acquainted with. It is true, that it in some measure resembles alumine, namely, in its softness to the touch, its adhesion to the tongue, its levity, its solubility in potash, and its precipitation from its solutions by ammoniac. But it differs from alumine in its other properties. Its combinations with acids have a very saccharine taste; it has a stronger affinity with those solvents; it does not afford alum with the sulphuric acid and the potash; it is totally soluble in carbonate of ammoniac; and lastly, it is not, like alumine, precipitable from its solutions by the oxalate and the tartrite of potash.

This earth being soluble in caustic potash, like alumine, we can no longer trust to this simple character to ascertain the presence of the latter earth; for it may happen that the earth of beryl should be taken for alumine, or a mixture of both for one or the other of these pure earths. It will therefore be necessary, whenever an earth soluble in potash is found, to endeavour to convert it into alum by the known methods. If it does not afford alum, it may certainly be concluded that it is not alumine. But it may possibly afford alum, and nevertheless contain the earth of beryl; a mother water will then remain, in which this last earth will be suspended.

To separate the small quantity of alum, which likewise remains in this mother water, it will be proper to decompose it by a solution of the carbonate of ammoniac added in excess; by this means alum will be entirely precipitated, and the earth of beryl will remain dissolved in the carbonate of ammoniac. This earth may afterwards be readily separated, by boiling the solution for a certain time. The heat will drive off the carbonate of ammoniac, and the earth will fall down in the form of a powder.

By comparing the results of the analysis of the beryl with those which Klaproth and myself obtained from that of the emerald, we might conclude, that these two stones are very different from each other; for I found that the emerald was composed of 64 of silex, 29 alumine, 2 lime, between 3 and 4 of the oxide of chrome, and 1 or 2 of water; whereas the beryl is composed of 69 silex, 21 alumine, 8 of the peculiar earth, and 1½ of the oxide of iron.

But since that time I have found that the emerald likewise contains this new earth; whence it follows, that the emerald and the beryl are one and the same substance, differing only in their colouring matter.

With regard to the proportion in which I have obtained this earth of the beryl, I do not give it as strictly accurate; for it is possible that part may have been dissolved at the same time as the alumine by the potash.[1]

I have not yet thought it proper to give a name to this earth. I shall wait till its properties are better known; besides which, I should be glad to have the advice of my brother-chemists on the subject.[2]

Newer Knowledge About Beryllium

→ BERYLLIUM was studied intensively in research projects leading up to the development of the atomic bomb, on account of its low atomic weight and low neutron-absorption cross-section. It was found that, theoretically, beryllium would be as good a moderator as graphite, but, on account of its scarcity its use did not prove practical. Beryllium is used in the laboratory as a neutron source when activated by a small amount of radium. Beryllium compounds are frequently used inside the tubes of fluorescent lights. The handling of these compounds has, however, been found hazardous because they are poisonous. Beryllium is another of the elements which throw the body's chemistry out of gear.

[1] Since the above was written, I have ascertained, that there was in fact a certain quantity of the earth of beryl dissolved by the potash with the alumine; and that instead of 8 per cent, the beryl contains 16.

[2] The most characteristic property of this earth, confirmed by the latest experiments of our colleague, being, that it forms salts of a saccharine taste, we propose to call it Glucine, sweet. . . . Note of the Editors of the Annales.

Barium, Strontium, Calcium, Magnesium

Excerpt from the following:
THE COLLECTED WORKS *of Humphry Davy, Vol. IV: Elements of Chemical Philosophy, Edited by his brother, John Davy, London, 1840.*

Barium

1. There is a mineral substance found in Cumberland, Yorkshire, and other parts of Britain, called Witherite, or carbonate of baryta. By dissolving this substance in dilute solution of nitric acid, evaporating the solution to dryness, and heating the salt obtained to whiteness, a light fawn-coloured powder is procured, which is baryta or barium combined with oxygen. To obtain *barium*, a quantity of this substance is made into a paste, with water, and placed on a plate of platina; a cavity is made in the paste to receive a globule of mercury; the mercury is rendered negative, the platina positive, by means of a Voltaic battery, containing about 100 double plates.

In a short time an amalgam will be formed, consisting of mercury and barium. This amalgam must be introduced into a little tube made of glass free from lead, which must be bent in the form of a retort, filled with the vapour of naphtha, and hermetically sealed. Heat must be applied to the end of the tube containing the amalgam, till all the mercury has been driven off; there will remain a solid difficultly fusible metal, which is barium.

2. I first gained indications of the decomposition of baryta, in the end of October 1807, and I obtained an alloy of it with iron, in March, 1808. The process of electrifying mercury, in contact with the earth, was pointed out to me in the course of my inquiries, by MM. Berzelius and Pontin of Stockholm, in May 1808; and in the beginning of June in the same year, I obtained *the metal*.

3. Barium, as procured by heating the amalgam, appeared of a dark gray colour, with a lustre inferior to that of cast iron. It was considerably heavier than sulfuric acid, for though surrounded by globules of gas, it sunk immediately in that fluid. It instantly became covered with a crust of baryta, when exposed to air, and burnt with a deep red light when gently heated. When thrown into water it effervesced violently, disappeared, and the water was found to be a solution of baryta.

Barium as yet has been obtained only in very minute quantities. I have never possessed enough of it to ascertain its gen-

eral chemical and physical characters, and no experiments
upon it have been published by any other person.

4. From some results that I have obtained, it seems probable
that barium may be procured by chemical, as well as electrical
decomposition. When baryta, or the salt improperly called
muriate of baryta, ignited to whiteness, was exposed to the
agency of potassium, that metal being sent through it in
vapour, a dark gray substance appeared, diffused through the
baryta, or the muriate, not volatile, that effervesces copiously
in water, and that lost its metallic appearance by exposure to
air:—the potassium in this process was converted into potassa.

5. The only well-known combination of barium with oxygen
is *baryta,* or *baria.* It is of a pale grayish green colour. Its
specific gravity is about 4, that of water being 1. This substance is a non-conductor of electricity, has a strong caustic
taste, reddens turmeric, and renders green vegetable blues.
When acted upon by a small quantity of water, it heats violently, becomes white, unites to a proportion of water, and becomes a hydrate. The pure alkaline earth is infusible, except by
an intense heat: the hydrate fuses at a strong red heat; a
considerable part of its water is expelled by a still higher
temperature. Baryta is soluble at 60°, in about 20 parts of
water, and at 212° in about 2 parts. That baryta is composed
of barium and oxygen, is proved by the combustion of barium
in oxygen; in which as I have found, oxygen is absorbed, and
no product but baryta formed. It is likewise proved synthetical-
ly by the action of barium upon water, in which case hydrogen
is evolved; and analytically it appears from the action of potassium on the earth. From indirect experiments, I am inclined
to consider baryta as composed of 89·7 of barium, and 10·3 of
oxygen: and supposing the earth to consist of one proportion
of metal and one of oxygen, the number representing barium
will be 130, and that representing the alkaline earth will be
145.

Barium, as would appear from the experiments of MM.
Gay-Lussac and Thenard, is capable of combining with more
oxygen than exists in baryta. These able chemists state, that
when baryta is gently heated by a spirit lamp, in a glass tube
filled with oxygen gas, an absorption of the gas takes place.
As yet no experiments have been made on the properties of
this *oxide of barium,* or on the quantity of oxygen it contains;
probably baryta may be easily combined with oxygen, by heating it with hyper-oxymuriate of baryta. *The hydrate of baryta,*
if its composition be estimated from M. Berthollet's experiments, consists of one proportion of baryta, and one of water.

6. One combination only of barium and chlorine is known;
it may be formed by heating baryta in muriatic acid gas, or in
chlorine. In the first case, the oxygen of the bartya produces
water by combining with the hydrogen of the acid; in the second it is expelled: and in an experiment made on purpose, I

found that for every part in volume of chlorine absorbed, half a part of oxygen was given off from the alkaline earth. Hence it may be concluded that the compound of barium and chlorine contains one proportion of metal 130, and one of chlorine 67.* This substance is fusible by a very strong heat, is very soluble in water; its taste is bitter, its colour white, it is crystalline and transparent. It is improperly called in the French nomenclature, muriate of baryta. According to the principles of nomenclature which I have proposed, its name will be *barane*.[1]

8. No other combinations of barium, except those with oxygen and chlorine, have been as yet examined; there can, however, be little doubt that its powers of combination will be, in many respects, analogous to those of potassium and sodium, as, of all metallic substances, it is the nearest related to these bodies.

9. The compounds of barium have as yet been applied to the arts in very few cases. Baryta is employed in small quantities, in the manufacture of certain kinds of porcelain; most of the salts containing baryta as a basis, are poisonous. The combination of baryta and carbonic acid, made artificially by pouring a solution of carbonate of ammonia into a solution of nitrate of baryta, forms a pigment of a very pure white colour.

Strontium

1. *Strontium* may be procured precisely in the same manner as barium; carbonate of strontia, or strontianite, a mineral found at Strontian in Scotland, being used instead of witherite. I first procured this metal in 1808, but in quantities too small to make an accurate examination of its properties. It seemed very analogous to barium, had not a very high lustre, appeared fixed, difficultly fusible, and not volatile. It became converted into strontia by exposure to air, and when thrown into water, decomposed it with great violence, producing hydrogen gas, and making the water a solution of strontia.

2. One combination of strontium with oxygen only is at present known; it is *strontia*, or strontites, the substance procured by burning strontium.[2] It may be produced in large quantities by igniting strontianite intensely with charcoal powder, or by heating to whiteness the salt formed from this fossil, by the action of nitric acid. It appears of a light fawn colour, and agrees in many of its characters with baryta. It is fusible only by an intense heat. Its specific gravity is between three and four, water being one. It is soluble in about 200 parts of

---

* The author was in error by assuming the formula to be BaCl instead of BaCl₂.—Editor's note.
[1] Chloride of barium.
Many attempts were made by early chemists to coin a one-word name for each compound of an element. They have nearly all been abandoned.—Editor.
[2] A peroxide may be obtained in the same manner as the peroxide of barium.

water, at common temperatures, and is much more soluble in hot than cold water; its taste is acrid and alkaline, it reddens paper tinged with turmeric. When acted upon by a small quantity of water it becomes hot, its colour changes to white, and it is converted into a hydrate, and then becomes fusible at a white heat. From indirect experiments, I am disposed to regard it as composed of about 86 of strontium and 14 oxygen; and supposing it to contain one proportion of metal and one of oxygen, the number representing strontium will be 90, and that representing the earth 105.

3. No experiments have as yet been made on the direct combination of strontium and chlorine; but a substance which appears to consist of these two bodies, and no other elements, may be made by heating strontia strongly in chlorine, or muriatic acid gas, or by igniting to whiteness the salt formed by the solution of strontianite in muriatic acid. By the action of chlorine on strontia, oxygen is expelled: by the action of muriatic acid gas upon it, water is formed. The compound of chlorine and strontium, or *strontane*,[s] is a white substance, difficultly fusible, fixed in the fire, a non-conductor of electricity, and of a peculiar bitter taste; when brought in contact with the flame of wax, tallow, oil, or alcohol, it tinges it of a rose colour; and this is a distinctive character of the compounds of strontium; the salts formed from it give this tint to flame, those of baryta give a yellow tint. From direct experiments I ascertained that 50 parts of strontane consisted of about 29 parts of metal and 21 of chlorine; so that it must be regarded as composed of one proportion of strontium, and one of chlorine, 90 and 67.

4. No experiments have as yet been made on the action of strontium, on any of the other elementary substances.

5. None of the compounds of this body have as yet been applied to any of the purposes of the arts, and its combinations are rare in nature.

Calcium

1. *Calcium* may be obtained by the same processes as barium and strontium. Mild calcareous earth, or chalk being used instead of witherite and strontianite; or common well-burnt lime may be employed for making the paste, from which the mercurial amalgam is to be formed by Voltaic electricity.

I first procured calcium about the same time as barium and strontium, but only in very minute quantities, so that little can be said concerning its nature. It appeared brighter and whiter than these two metals, and burnt, when gently heated, producing dry lime. I have had no opportunity of examining its general physical and chemical qualities.

2. There is only one known combination of calcium and

[s] Chloride of strontium.

oxygen, which is the important substance, *lime* or *calcia*. The nature of this substance is proved by the phenomena of the combustion of calcium; the metal becomes converted into the earth, with the absorption of oxygen gas. When the amalgam of calcium is thrown into water, hydrogen gas is disengaged, and the water becomes a solution of lime; and from the quantity of hydrogen gas disengaged, compared with the quantity of lime formed in experiments of this kind, M. Berzelius has endeavoured to ascertain the proportion of oxygen in lime. The nature of lime may be also proved by analysis; when potassium in vapour is sent through the earth, ignited to whiteness, the potassium, I have found, becomes potassa, and a dark gray substance of metallic splendour, which is calcium either wholly or partly deprived of oxygen, is found embedded in the potassa, and it effervesces violently, and forms a solution of lime, by the action of water.

Lime is obtained for common purposes, from marble of the whitest kind such as Parian or Carara marble, by long exposure to a strong heat. It is a white soft substance, of specific gravity 2·3. It requires an intense degree of heat for its fusion, and has not yet been rendered volatile. Its taste is analogous to, but milder than that of baryta and strontia. It is soluble in about 450 parts of water, and seems to be more soluble in cold than in hot water. It acts upon vegetable colours in a manner similar to the other alkaline earths. When water, in small quantities, is added to it, a considerable heat is produced, a portion of the water combines with the lime, and it becomes a hydrate; but water does not adhere to it with the same degree of energy, as to baria and strontia, for it may be expelled by a strong red heat. From the experiments of M. Berzelius, and those which I have made, it appears that lime consists of about 20 of metal to 7·5 of oxygen, and the number representing calcium is 40, and that representing lime 55; and the *hydrate of lime* must consist of 55 lime and 17 water, which estimation agrees with the experiments of M. Lavoisier and Mr. Dalton.

I have attempted to combine lime with more oxygen, but without success.

3. When lime is heated strongly in contact with chlorine, oxygen is expelled, and chlorine absorbed; and, as happens in all the decompositions of metallic oxides, of which the metals combine with only one proportion of oxygen and chlorine, for every two in volume of chlorine absorbed, a volume of oxygen is expelled. The substance formed by the action of chlorine on lime, as the oxygen of the lime is expelled, must evidently consist of chlorine and calcium. It has been called dry muriate of lime; according to the true view of its composition, it may be called *calcane*.[4] It is a semi-transparent crystalline substance, fusible at a strong red heat, a non-conductor of electricity, has a very bitter taste, rapidly absorbs water from the atmosphere;

4 Chloride of calcium.

and is extremely soluble in water: by the evaporation of its solution at a low heat, crystals may be obtained, which consist of calcane, combined with more than a third their weight of water. From my experiments, it appears that calcane consists of 31 chlorine and 19 of calcium, and hence it may be supposed to contain one proportion of the metal, and one of the gas, and the number representing it on this idea is 107; and it is evident, from the experiment on the action of chlorine on lime, that the proportion of oxygen in lime, and of chlorine in calcane, must be in the ratio of 15 to 67.

4. As yet no experiments have been made on the combinations of calcium with any of the inflammable, or acidiferous substances, or metals.

5. The compounds of calcium are found abundantly on the surface of the globe, and are of great importance in the economy of nature, and in the processes of art. Lime combined with carbonic acid is an essential part of fertile lands: a number of rocks are constituted by this substance. Gypsum or alabaster, is lime combined with sulphuric acid; and the earth of bones consists of lime united to phosphoric acid. There is no animal or vegetable substance that does not contain larger or smaller quantities of calcareous matter. The uses of lime in mortar are well known. Quicklime, employed as a manure, tends to decompose[5] and dissolve inert vegetable matter, and renders it proper for the nourishment of plants; and in this operation the lime is united to carbonic acid, and becomes a permanent part of the soil. In the process of tanning, lime is employed to remove the hair from the skins of animals, and it is used in certain operations of bleaching, dyeing, and other useful arts.

Magnesium

1. *Magnesium*[6] may be procured from the earth called magnesia, which is the same as the calcined magnesia of druggists, by processes similar to those referred to in the three preceding sections; but a much longer time is required to produce an amalgam of magnesium and quicksilver, by electrical powers, than to produce amalgams of the metals of the other alkaline earths.

I succeeded in decomposing magnesia likewise, in the following manner: I passed potassium in vapour through magnesia, heated to intense whiteness, in a tube of platinum, out of the contact of air; I then introduced a small quantity of mercury, and heated it gently for some time in the tube. An amal-

[5] According to the results of my experiment on the action of lime on animal and vegetable substances, it does not decompose, but preserves the majority of them.
[6] In my first paper on the decomposition of the earths, published in 1808, I called the metal from magnesia, magnium, fearing lest, if called magnesium, it should be confounded with the name formerly applied to manganese. The candid criticisms of some philosophical friends have induced me to apply the termination in the usual manner.

gam was obtained, which by distillation, out of the contact of the atmosphere, afforded a dark gray metallic film, which was infusible at the point at which plate glass softened, and which, in the process of distillation of the mercury, rendered the glass black at its point of contact with it. This film burnt when heated strongly, with a red light, and became converted into a white powder, which had the character of magnesia: when a portion of the metal was thrown into water, it sunk to the bottom, and effervesced slowly, becoming covered with a white powder; by adding a little muriatic acid to the water, the effervescence was violent; the metal rapidly disappeared, and the solution was found to contain magnesia.

I have made several experiments with the hope of obtaining larger quantities of magnesium, such as might have enabled me to examine its chemical and physical properties; but without success.[7] It is very difficult to procure a pure amalgam of magnesium by potassium and mercury; the heat must be intense; and at a high temperature, potassium acts with great energy upon platina, so that unless the tube is very solid, it is destroyed in the process, and when the heat is not very great, potassium remains in the tube, which is found afterwards in the amalgam. The potassium may, however, be separated by the action of water; which, even in the amalgam, rapidly converts it into potassa, but which has a much feebler action on magnesium. When the amalgam contains potassium, it likewise usually contains platinum, which is very soluble in the compound of potassium and quicksilver.

There is only one known compound of magnesium and oxygen, which is the substance from which the metal is procured, *Magnesia*. That magnesia consists of magnesium and oxygen, is proved both by analysis and synthesis. In the production of magnesium by potassium, the potassium is found converted into potassa, and therefore must have gained oxygen from the magnesia; and in the formation of magnesia from magnesium, oxygen is absorbed. No experiments have as yet been made to determine the proportions of the elements in magnesia; but from experiments which I have made on the combinations of this substance with acids, assuming that they are single proportions, I am inclined to adopt 43 as the number representing it; and if it be supposed to be constituted by 1 proportion of metal, and 1 of oxygen, the number representing the metal will be 28.

Magnesia appears in its common form, as a white soft powder; its specific gravity is between 2 and 3. It is found in nature in the crystalline form; specimens have been brought from North America, which nearly resemble talc in their external characters. Magnesia has scarcely any taste, no smell; it reddens turmeric. It is infusible; except by the intense heat pro-

---

[7] M. Bussy has been successful, by heating together potassium and chloride of magnesium. This metal is not unlike silver in appearance; it is malleable, and fusible at a red heat.

duced by the combustion of hydrogen gas in oxygen, or that generated by Voltaic electricity. It is scarcely soluble in water, but produces heat when water is mixed with it, and absorbs a considerable portion of the fluid. When it is procured by the decomposition of a solution in which it is combined with an acid, by means of solution of potassa or soda, it falls down in union with water, as a hydrate; but the water adheres to it with a very feeble atraction only, and is expelled entirely at a red heat. *Hydrate of magnesia* when dried at 212°, appears in coherent semi-transparent masses, very brittle and soft; it contains about ¼ of its weight of water.

3. When magnesia is strongly heated in contact with chlorine, chlorine is absorbed, and oxygen expelled, and in the usual proportions as to volume. Hence it is evident that there exists a combination of magnesium and chlorine; though this body, which may be called *magnesane*,[8] has never been examined in a separate state. The salt called muriate of magnesia, is a compound of magnesane and water, and when it is acted on by a strong red heat, by far the greatest part of the chlorine unites to the hydrogen of the water, and rises in the form of muriatic acid gas, and the oxygen of the decomposed water combines with the magnesium to form magnesia; some magnesane is, however, found mixed with the magnesia, which affords crystals of muriate of magnesia by the action of water.

4. No experiments have as yet been made on the action of magnesium upon any of the inflammable or metallic substances.

5. The compounds of magnesium occur extensively diffused in nature. Magnesia exists in certain limestones which are found in different parts of Great Britain and Ireland, and which are less fitted for the general purposes of manure than common limestone. Magnesia, in its uncombined state, as appears from the experiments of Mr. Tennant, is injurious to plants, but united to carbonic acid, it seems to form an useful part of the soil: the magnesium limestones are distinguished by their slow solution in acids; and they render weak solutions of nitric acid turbid by their action upon them. Magnesia, and some of its saline combinations are used in medicine; its application in bleaching has been referred to in an early part of this work.

[8] Chloride of magnesium.

Radioactivity

Excerpt from the following:
RAYONS ÉMIS PAR LES COMPOSÉS DE L'URANIUM ET DU THORIUM (*Rays emitted by compounds of uranium and thorium.*) *Note de Mme. Sklodowska Curie*[1], *présentée par M. Lippmann, Comptes rendus, Vol. 126, April, 1898.*

➤ I HAVE STUDIED the conductivity of air under the influence the rays from uranium, discovered by M. Becquerel, and I have sought whether any other bodies than those composed of uranium are able to render air a conductor of electricity. I used for this study a plate condenser; one of the plates was covered with a uniform layer of uranium or another substance finely pulverized. (Diameter of the plates 8cm.; distance 3 cm.) A difference of potential of 100 volts was established between the plates. The current which passed through the condenser was measured in absolute value by means of an electrometer and a piezo-electric quartz.

I have examined a great number of metals, salts, oxides and minerals[2]. The Table, given below gives, for each substance, the value of the current i in amperes (of the order of 10^{-11}). Materials which I have studied which do not appear in the Table are at least 100 times less active than uranium.

All the compounds of uranimum studied are active and they are, in general, the more active the more uranium they contain.

The compounds of thorium are very active. The oxide of thorium even exceeds metallic thorium in activity.

It should be noted that the two most active elements, uranium and thorium, are those which have the greatest atomic weight.

White phosphorus is very active, but its activity is probably of a different nature than that of uranium and thorium. In fact, phosphorus is not active either in the state of red phosphorus or of the phosphates.

The minerals which have shown themselves active contain active elements. Two ores of uranium, pitchblende (uranium oxide) and chalcolite (phosphate of copper and uranium) are much more active than uranium itself. This fact is very re-

[1] This work was done at the Municipal School of Industrial Physics and Chemistry.
[2] The uranium used for this study was donated by M. Moissan. The salts and oxides were pure compounds, tested at the laboratory of M. Etard at the School of Physics and Chemistry. M. Lacroix was kind enough to get me some mineral specimens of known composition, from the collection of the Museum. Some rare and pure oxides were given by M. Demarçay. I wish to thank these gentlemen for their kindness.

TABLE

	AMPÈRES
Uranium, slightly carbonated	24 x 10^{-12}
Black oxide of uranium, U_2O_5	27 "
Green oxide of uranium, U_3O_8	18 "
Uranates of ammonia, potassium, sodium, about	12 "
Hydrated uranic acid	6 "
Uranyl nitrate, uranous sulfate, uranyl and potassium sulfate, about	7 "
Artificial chalcolite (copper and uranium phosphate)	9 "
Thorium oxide in a layer 0.25 mm thick	22 "
Thorium oxide in a layer 6 mm thick	53 "
Thorium sulfate	8 "
Potassium fluoxytantalate	2 "
Potassium fluoxyniobate and cerium oxide	0.3 "
Pitchblende from Johanngeorgenstadt	83 "
Pitchblende from Cornwall	16 "
Pitchblende from Joachimsthal and from Pzibran	67 "
Natural chalcolite	52 "
Autunite	27 "
Various Thorites	2 to 14 "
Orangite	20 "
Samarskite	11 "
Fergusonite, monazite, xenotime, niobite, aeschinite	3 to 7 "
Cleveite, very active.	

markable and leads to the belief that these minerals may contain an element much more active than uranium. I have produced chalcolite by the process of Debray from pure materials, this artificial chaloclite is no more active than any other salt of uranium.

Absorption.—The effects produced by active substances increase with the thickness of the layer used. This increase is very feeble for compounds of uranium; it is considerable for the oxide of thorium which seems to be partly transparent to the rays which it emits.

To study the transparency of different substances, a thin plate of one of them is placed over the active layer. The absorption is always very great. Nevertheless rays pass through thin sheets of metal, glass, ebonite, and paper. The fraction of rays transmitted by aluminum foil 0.01 mm thick is:

0.2 for uranium, ammonium uranate, uranous oxide, artificial chalcolite.
0.33 for pitchblende and natural chalcolite.
0.4 for thorium oxide and thorium sulfate 0.5 mm thick.
0.7 for thorium oxide 6 mm thick.

It is evident that compounds of the same metal emit rays absorbed equally. The rays emitted by thorium are more penetrating than those emitted by uranium; also, thorium oxide in a thick layer emits much more penetrating rays than it emits in a thin layer.

Photographic impressions.—I have obtained good photographic impressions with uranium, uranous oxide, pitchblende, chalcolite, and thorium oxide. These bodies are active at a short distance to pass through either air or glass or aluminum. Thorium sulfate gives weaker impressions and potassium fluoxytantalate very weak impressions.

Analogy with the secondary rays of Röntgen rays.—The properties of rays emitted by uranium and thorium are very analogous to the secondary rays of Röntgen rays, studied recently by M. Sagnac. I have proved especially that, under the action of Röntgen rays, uranium, pitchblende and thorium oxide emit secondary rays which, from the point of view of the discharge of electrified bodies, have generally more effect than the secondary rays of lead. Among the metals studied by M. Sagnac, uranium and thorium would be placed beside or beyond lead.

To interpret the spontaneous radiation of uranium and thorium one might imagine that all space is constantly traversed by rays analogous to Röntgen rays but much more penetrating and able to be absorbed only by certain elements of high atomic weight, such as uranium and thorium.

Radium

Excerpt from the following:
SUR UNE NOUVELLE SUBSTANCE FORTEMENT RADIO-ACTIVE, *Contenue Dans La Pechblende*[3]. *(On a new strongly radio-active substance contained in pitchblend). Note de M. P. Curie, de Mme. P. Curie et da M. G. Bémont, présentée par M. Becquerel, Comptes rendus, Vol. 127, December, 1898.*

→ Two of us have shown that, by purely chemical processes, it is possible to extract from pitchblend a strongly radio-active substance. This substance is closely related to bismuth in its analytical properties. We have put forth the opinion that pitchblend perhaps contains a new element, for which we have proposed the name *polonium*[4].

The researches which we are carrying through actually are in agreement with the first results obtained; but, during

[3] This work was done at the Municipal School of Industrial Physics and Chemistry.
[4] M. P. Curie and Mme. P. Curie, Comptes Rendus, t. CXXVII, p. 175.

these researches, we have found a second substance strongly
radio-active and entirely different from the first in its chemical
properties. In fact, polonium is precipitated from acid solution by hydrogen sulfide; its salts are soluble in acids, and
water precipitates them from these solutions; polonium is
completely precipitated by ammonia.

The new radio-active substance which we have found has
all the chemical properties of fairly pure barium: it is not
precipitated by hydrogen sulfide, nor by ammonium sulfide,
nor by ammonia; the sulfate is insoluble in water and in acids;
the carbonate is insoluble in water; the chloride, very soluble
in water, is insoluble in concentrated hydrochloric acid and
in alcohol. Finally this substance gives the spectrum of barium,
easily recognizable.

We believe nevertheless that this substance, although composed in the greater part of barium, contains besides a new
element which communicates radio-activity to it and which,
moreover, is a very close relative of barium in its chemical
properties.

Here are the reasons which plead in favor of this way of
looking at it:

1. Barium and its compounds are not ordinarily radio-active; but, one of us has shown that radio-activity seems to be
a property of the atom, persisting in all chemical and physical
states of matter[5]. From this point of view, the radio-activity of
our material would not be due to barium but ought to be
attributed to another element.

2. The first substances which we obtained had, in the state
of the hydrochloride, a radio-activity 60 times greater than
that of metallic uranium (the radio-active intensity being
measured by the amount of conductability of the air in our
apparatus at the plates). By dissolving the chlorides in water
and precipitating a part with alcohol, the part precipitated
is much more active than the part remaining in solution. Based
on this fact, it is possible to carry out a series of fractionations permitting us to obtain more and more active chlorides.
We have thus obtained chlorides having an activity 900 times
as great as that of uranium. We have been struck by the
scarcity of the substance and, after the course of the operations, we can predict that the activity would have been greatly
increased if we had been able to continue. These facts can
only be explained by the presence of a radio-active element
whose chloride is less soluble in dilute alcohol than that of
barium.

3. M. Demarçay has been good enough to examine the
spectrum of our substance, with a kindness for which we can
never thank him enough. The results of his examination are
given in a special note following ours. M. Demarçay has
found in the spectrum a line which does not seem to be due
[5] Mme. P. Curie, Comptes Rendus, t. CXXVI, p. 1101.

to any known element. This line, faintly visible with the chloride 60 times as active as uranium, has become notable with the chloride enriched by fractionation up to activity 900 times uranium. The intensity of this line increases at the same time as the radio-activity, and this is, we think, a very serious reason to attribute it to the radio-active part of our substance.

The different reasons which we have enumerated lead us to believe that the new radio-active substance contains a new element to which we propose to give the name *radium*.

We have determined the atomic weight of our active barium, by determining the chlorine in the anhydrous chloride. We have found numbers which differ very little from those obtained in duplicate with inactive barium chloride; although the values for the active barium are always a little greater, still the difference is of the order of magnitude of experimental error.

The new radio-active substance certainly contains a very great proportion of barium; in spite of that, the radio-activity is considerable. The radio-activity of radium must therefore be enormous.

Uranium, thorium, polonium, radium and their compounds make air a conductor of electricity and act photographically upon sensitized plates. From these two points of view, polonium and radium are considerably more active than uranium and thorium. Good images are obtained on photographic plates with radium and polonium with a half-minute exposure; several hours are necessary to obtain the same result with uranium and thorium.

The rays emitted by the compounds of polonium and radium render barium platinocyanide fluorescent; their action, from this point of view, is analogous to that of Röntgen rays, but considerably weaker. To make the experiment, place upon the active substance a very thin piece of aluminum foil, upon which is spread a thin layer of barium platinocyanide; in the dark the platinocyanide appears freebly luminous in the presence of the active substance.

We realize, therefore, a source of light, to tell the truth very feeble, but one which functions without a source of energy. Here is a contradiction more or less apparent, with the principle of Carnot.

Uranium and thorium do not give any light under these conditions, their action being probably too feeble[6].

[6] We ask permission to thank here M. Suess, Correspondent of the Institute, Professor at the University of Vienna. Through his good offices, we have obtained from the Austrian government, gratis, a shipment of 100 kg. of residue from the treatment of pitchblend at Joachimsthal, containing no uranium but containing polonium and radium. This gift has facilitated our research greatly.

Spectral Line of Radium

SUR LE SPECTRE D'UNE SUBSTANCE RADIO-ACTIVE (*On the spectrum of a radio-active substance.*) Note de M. Eug. Demarçay. *Comptes rendus, Dec. 26, 1898.*

→ M. AND MME. CURIE have asked me to examine, with respect to the spectrum, a substance containing principally some barium chloride and in which they claim, for reasons set forth elsewhere, the presence of a new element. This substance, dissolved in distilled water slightly acidulated with HCl and submitted to the action of the spark of my coil on a heavy wire, gave a brilliant spectrum which was photographed. For that purpose I made two plates with two different times of exposure, one twice the other. These two plates have given, morever, according to the intensity of the lines, identically the same result. I have measured them and I am able to see:

1. Barium represented with great intensity by its strong and faint lines;

2. Lead recognizable from its principal lines rather faint besides;

3. Platinum due to the electrodes and the principal lines of calcium due to the solvent;

4. A *notable* line stronger than the weak lines of barium having for λ : 3814.8 (Rowland's scale). It does not seem possible to me that this line can be attributed to any known element: first, because there does not appear on the plates in question any other line than those enumerated above, save some feeble lines from the air, which excludes all the other simple bodies which have only, at most, rather weak lines in the neighborhood of 3814; in the second place, and in addition, because the method of purification employed for the substance excludes precisely the presence of those which might be able to cause them (Fe, Cr, Co, Ni, - - -) and which, moreover, do not show any lines, weak or strong. Neither barium nor lead from elsewhere, as I have assured myself, give any line which coincides with it .

It has been measured by comparison with two lines of platinum 3818.9 and 3801.5 which surround it. It is near and distinct from a bismuth line of moderate intensity.

The Elements of Group III

Group IIIα

ELEMENT   ELECTRON SHELLS

$$_5B = K_2L_3$$
$$_{13}Al = K_2L_8M_3$$
$$_{31}Ga = K_2L_8M_{18}N_3$$
$$_{49}In = K_2L_8M_{18}N_{18}O_3$$
$$_{81}Tl = K_2L_8M_{18}N_{32}O_{18}P_3$$

Group IIIb

$$_{21}Sc = K_2L_8M_9N_2$$
$$_{39}Y = K_2L_8M_{18}N_9O_2$$
$$_{57}La = K_2L_8M_{18}N_{18}O_9P_2$$
$$_{89}Ac = K_2L_8M_{18}N_{32}O_{18}P_9Q_2$$

→THE QUALITY of alkalinity, so strong in the Group I metals and still marked in those of Group II, has become very weak in Group III. The hydroxide of aluminum has the inbetween property of being amphoteric. In some cases it acts like a mild base, in others like a weak acid. Boron, the first member of the group, does not form the hydroxide, but forms two acids noted for their extreme weakness. They are H_3BO_3, orthoboric, sometimes called "boracic" acid, and $H_2B_4O_7$, tetra- or pyroboric acid, of which borax is a salt ($Na_2B_4O_7$).

Scandium, Yttrium and Lanthanum have the properties characteristic of the Rare Earth elements, which due to their following Lanthanum, are now known as the Lanthanide elements. Actinium, an element known chiefly for its radioactive properties, introduces the second series of similar elements, paralleling the Rare Earths. They are called, after it, the Actinide Series of elements.

All these elements, except boron, are recognized analytically by their insoluble but gelatinous, colloidal white hydroxides. The properties are so similar chemically that no good separation is possible by conventional chemical techniques. The problem of separating them has, however, been solved by ion exchange methods.

Boron

Excerpt from the following:
ON THE DECOMPOSITION AND RECOMPOSITION OF BORIC
ACID, *by MM. Gay-Lussac and Thenard. In Annales de
Chimie, Paris, 30 Novembre, 1808.*

➤WE ANNOUNCED in a note to the Institute the 21st of last
June, and we published in the Bulletin of the Philomatic Society for the month of July, that in treating fluoric and boracic
acids with the metal potassium there are obtained results which
can be explained only by admitting that these acids are composed of a combustible body and oxygen. Nevertheless, since
we had never recomposed it, we added that we have never
claimed this composition as perfectly demonstrated. Since that
time, we have continued and varied our researches; and we
can state today that the composition of boracic acid is no
longer problematical. In fact we decompose and we recom-
pose this acid at will.

To decompose it, take equal parts of metal and of very pure
and vitreous boracic acid in a copper tube to which a tube of
bent glass is attached. Place the copper tube in a small furnace, with the end of the glass tube in a flask of mercury.
When the apparatus is ready, heat the copper tube little by
little until it becomes faintly red; hold it in this state for several
minutes; then, the operation being ended, allow it to cool and
take out the material. Here are the phenomena which are observed in this experiment.

When the temperature is about 150 degrees, all at once the
mixture glows strongly, which appears in a striking manner if
a glass tube is used. So much heat is produced that the glass
tube cracks and sometimes breaks, and the air is almost always
driven out of the vessel with force. From the beginning to the
end of the experiment only atmospheric is released with a few
bubbles of hydrogen gas which do not amount to the 50th
part of that given off when the metal combines with water.
The metal is used up by decomposing part of the boracic
acid; and these two substances are converted by their mutual
reaction, into an olive gray material which is a mixture of
potassium, potassium borate and the radicle of boracic acid.
Extract this mixture in a tube by pouring water onto it and
heating slowly, and separate the boracic radicle by washing
with water cold or hot[1]; that which does not dissolve is the
radicle itself, which shows the following properties.

[1] Before washing, it is well to neutralize with muriatic acid the alkali
which the solution contains; for it prevents the boracic acid being oxidized,
and thus dissolved in the liquid to which it gives a very deep color.

This radicle is a greenish-brown, fixed and insoluble in water; it has no taste, it has no effect upon the color of either litmus or syrup of violets. Mixed with potassium chlorate or potassium nitrate and projected into a red-hot crucible, a vivid combustion results, of which boracic acid is one of the products. When it is treated with nitric acid a great effervescence results, even in the cold, and when the liquid is evaporated, much boracic acid is obtained. But of all the phenomena produced by the boracic radicle in its contact with other substances, the most curious and the most important are those which it presents with oxygen.

On projecting three decigrams of boracic radicle into a silver crucible at a faint red heat, and covering this crucible with a bell-jar of about a liter and a half capacity, full of oxygen and standing over mercury, it usually burns and the mercury rises so rapidly that it suddenly fills half the bell-jar. Nevertheless, in this experiment the combustion of the boracic acid radicle is far from complete. That which prevents it is that the radicle passes almost entirely into the state of a black oxide, which we believe we are the first to recognize, and, the outer parts of this oxide then passing into the state of boracic acid, this remains and so prevents the inner part from coming in contact with the oxygen. So, to burn it completely, it is necessary to wash it, and put it again in contact with oxygen gas, always at a cherry-red heat. But this time it burns with less force and absorbs less oxygen than the first time, because it is already oxidized; and the exterior part always passes into the state of boracic acid which remains, hindering the combustion of the interior: so to convert all to boracic acid, it is necessary to submit it to a great number of successive ignitions and to as many washings.

In all these combustions, there is always fixation of oxygen without liberation of any gas; and all give acid as the product. Upon treating these products with boiling water there is obtained by suitable evaporation and cooling crystallized boracic acid, of which we have presented a sample to the Institute.

Finally, the boracic acid radicle behaves in air just as in oxygen, with the difference only that the combustion is less lively.

It follows then from all these experiments that boracic acid is actually composed of oxygen and a combustible body. We have proved conclusively that this body, which we now propose to call bore, is of a definite nature, which can be placed beside carbon, phosphorus, and sulphur; and we are led to think that to pass into the state of boracic acid it requires a great quantity of oxygen.

Aluminum

Excerpt from the following:
ON ALUMINUM, *by F. Wöhler. In Annalen der Physik und Chemie, Leipzig, 1827.*

To LEARN to know the physical and chemical properties of the elements which in the oxidized state make up the greater part of the surface of the earth, is from many points of view of greater interest than the study of many of the true metals; for upon our knowledge of these bodies depends in part our ability to imagine the formation of the earth's surface from the original material of volcanic eruptions and so forth.—Of all the radicles in the earth-substances in the most abundant kinds of soil, we have up to now learned to know only kiesel-earth, through Berzelius' experiments. H. Davy seems to have separated the radicle of clay, both by the agency of the electric battery upon a fused mixture of clay and potash, and by the action of potassium vapor upon clay at white heat. But in both cases it did not occur to him to separate the reduced metal from the remaining mass; so he could not have studied its properties.

Some years ago Oersted discovered an easy method of combining chlorine with the radicle of clay, by the application of a very ingenious method, which consists of allowing chlorine gas to stream over incandescent clay mixed with powdered charcoal. From this compound there is obtained then, by means of potassium amalgam, an amalgam of aluminum, which oxidizes very quickly in air, and by distillation of the mercury the remaining aluminum can be recovered. Of the aluminum so obtained he says only that it was a lump of metal, of the color and luster of tin.

I have repeated this experiment of Oersted's, but got no positive result from it. By distillation of the potassium amalgam, after it was heated with the aluminum chloride, there remained at the end a gray molten mass of metal, which, however, evaporated when the heat was increased into a green vapor and distilled over as pure potassium. After this I looked around for another method, although I do not wish to say that it is not possible to reduce aluminum by this one.—Since Oersted noted at the end of his communication that he could not look upon his researches on aluminum as complete, it might seem, although many years have passed since then, as though I have forced my way into a research successfully begun by another but uncompleted, because they promise new and perhaps more brilliant results. I must remark here that

Herr Oersted himself encouraged me to pursue this research further.

Metallic Aluminum

The method for reducing and exhibiting this metal rests, it seems to me, on the decomposition of aluminum chloride by potassium and on the property of aluminum of not oxidizing in water. If a tiny piece of aluminum chloride be warmed in a glass tube with some potassium the violent reaction, accompanied by fire, shatters the tube. I then tried the reaction in a little platinum crucible, which succeeded very well. The reaction is always so violent that the cover must be fastened on with wire, so that it will not be thrown off, for the reaction, which gives off only a moderate amount of heat in the open, will suddenly of itself raise the crucible to red heat. Platinum will scarcely withstand it. On this account, to guard against possible contamination of the reduced aluminum with any platinum which may be lost, I always afterward made the reduction experiments in a little porcelain crucible, and went about it in the following way: Put into the bottom of the crucible a little piece of potassium free from carbonate, from which the kerosene clinging to it has been carefully removed. Cover this with a little piece of aluminum chloride of about the same volume. Then heat the crucible, covered with its lid, at first gently, until the combustion appears, which keeps going by itself, then strongly when this last is over. The largest piece of potassium with which I have attempted to work at one time up to now is ten balls the size of peas; in a Hessian crucible one could manage to operate with larger amounts. With these quantities the amounts of the reacting substances must be arranged so that either there is so much potassium that the reduced mass is alkaline, or so much excess aluminum chloride that it can be seen to evaporate at the moment of reduction.— The reduced mass is as a rule fully molten and blackish gray. The *fully* cooled crucible is dropped into a glass of water, in which the salt mass, under gentle heating, releases evil-smelling hydrogen gas and a gray powder separates, which on closer inspection especially in sunlight appears as composed of little scales of pure metal. After it has settled, pour the liquid off, put it on a filter, wash it with *cold* water and dry it. It is the metal aluminum.

Electrolytic Process

→BE IT KNOWN that I, CHARLES M. HALL, a citizen of the United States, residing at Oberlin, in the county of Lorain and State of Ohio, have invented or discovered certain new and useful Improvements in the Manufacture of Aluminium, of which improvements the following is a specification.

In applications filed by me July 9, 1886, and February 2, 1887, numbered 207,601 and 226,206, respectively, I have described and claimed certain processes for the reduction of aluminium, wherein I employ fluoride salts of aluminium or double fluorides of aluminium and electro-positive metals—as, for example, sodium or potassium—in a fused state to dissolve alumina, and the alumina is subjected to electrolysis when in a state of solution in the fused salts, thereby reducing aluminium at the negative electrode, the oxygen going to the positive electrode. The bath formed of the double fluoride of of aluminium and an alkaline metal, as described in the above application, becomes less efficient after being subjected to electrolytic action for some time. This change does not result from any removal of aluminium fluoride or of fluorine from the bath, as no fluorine is separated; but a black or dark substance is formed in the bath, apparently from the alkaline constituent of the same, which interferes with a free electrolytic action and increases the electrical resistance; hence it has been found necessary when employing the salts named to change the bath after a continuous use of the same.

The object of the invention described herein is to provide a bath wherein the reduction of aluminium from its oxide may be carried on continuously without diminution and without increasing the electro-motive force of the current.

Scandium

Excerpt from the following:
Sur le scandium, élément nouveau, (On Scandium, a new element), note de M. L. F. Nilson, présentée par M. Berthelot. Comptes rendus 88: Mar. 24, 1879.

➤THE PREPARATION of ytterbine, described in the preceding note, has given me an insoluble earth deposited as a subnitrate. On taking up the precipitate again in boiling water, it was found that the molecular weight was no longer 131, as it should have been from the data of M. Marignac, but 127.6. I concluded from this that an earth of molecular weight lower than 131 must have been mixed with the product examined. M. Thalén, who had the kindness to examine the spectrum, found that the chloride of this substance showed some lines unknown for elements already described, so I ventured to try to isolate the substance. To this end I made many partial decompositions of the nitrates and some determinations of the molecular weight of the earth deposited in the insoluble residues and containing the new substance, according to the methods indicated in my note about ytterbine.

For the element thus characterized, I propose the name *scandium*, which recalls its presence in gadolinite or in euxe-

nite, minerals which have been found so far only in the Scandinavian peninsula.

Recognition

Excerpt from the following:
SUR LE SCANDIUM, *(On Scandium) Note de M.P.T. Cleve
présentée par M. Wurtz. Comptes rendus 89: Aug. 18, 1879*

→AT THE MEETING of March 24, 1879, M. Nilson announced the discovery of a new element, which he calls *scandium*, which he has extracted from ytterbine. Some weeks after
that publication, I found the same metal in gadolinite and in
yttrotitanite from Norway. I have examined its characteristics
Here are the results:

At the present time, scandium has been found only in
gadolinite and in yttrotitanite. It is found in these two minerals
only in very small quantities. In gadolinite it constitutes only
0.002 to 0.003 g. per 100 of the oxide, and in yttrotitanite
0.005.

The only oxide which scandium forms, scandine, must have
the formula Sc_2O_3. The composition of the double ammonium
sulfate and of the double potassium oxalate prove the accuracy
of this formula, and the composition of the double potassium
sulfate, as well as of the selenite, establish it even better.

The atomic weight of scandium is, from this determination,
45.12. The atomic weight of scandium can be taken as 45.

The oxide of *Scandium, scandine*, Sc_2O_3, is a perfectly white
powder, soft, infusible, resembling magnesia. Acids, even the
strongest, attack it with difficulty, nevertheless it is more
soluble in acids than alumina. Sulfuric acid gives with scandine
a voluminous white mass of sulfate, recalling the appearance
of thorium sulfate when it is separated by heating. Hydrochloric acid dissolves more easily than nitric acid. The density
of the oxide is approximately 3.8.

The hydroxide of scandium is a white and voluminous precipitate, resembling aluminum hydroxide. It does not seem to
attract carbon dioxide from the air. Dried, it forms semi-transparent fragments. The hydroxide is insoluble in an excess of
ammonia and of caustic potash: It does not decompose ammonium chloride when it is heated with a solution of that
salt.

The salts of scandium are colorless or white. They have an
astringent and very bitter taste, very different from the sweetish
taste of the salts of yttria. The sulfate does not form distinct
crystals. The nitrate, the oxalate, the acetate and the formate
are crystallizable. . . .

Prediction Fulfilled

The interesting thing about the discovery of scandium is
that its existence has already been announced. In his memoir

on the periodic law, M. Mendeleeff[1] predicted the existence of a metal of atomic weight 44. He called it *ekaboron*. The characteristics of ekaboron correspond quite well with those of scandium.

Let us recall what the Russian scientist said about his hypothetical metal and compare the characteristics which he attributed to it with those of scandium.

[1] *Ann. der Chem. und Pharmacie, supplement. B. VIII, p. 133.*

Supposed Characteristics of Ekaboron

Observed Characteristics of Scandium

Atomic weight, 44.

Atomic weight, 45.

Ekaboron should have only one stable oxide, Eb_2O_3, a stronger base than alumina, with which it should have many characteristics in common. It should be less basic than magnesia.

Scandium forms only one oxide, Sc_2O_3, a much stronger base than alumina, but weaker than magnesia.

Although yttria ought to form a stronger base, one might predict a great resemblance between yttria and the oxide of ekaboron. If ekaboron should be mixed with yttria, their separation would be difficult and would be dependent upon slight differences, for example, on differences in solubilities, or differences in basicities.

Scandine is less basic than yttria, and their separation is dependent upon the difference in stability to heat of their nitrates.

The oxide of ekaboron is insoluble in alkalies; it is doubtful whether it will decompose ammonium chloride.

Scandium hydroxide is insoluble in alkalies; it does not decompose ammonium chloride.

Its salts should be colorless and give gelatinous precipitates with potassium hydroxide, sodium carbonate and sodium acid sulfate.

The salts of scandium are colorless and give gelatinous precipitates with potassium hydroxide, sodium carbonate and sodium acid sulfate.

With potassium sulfate it ought to form a double salt having the composition of alum, but scarcely isomorphous with that salt.

The double sulfate of scandium and ammonium is anhydrous, but otherwise it has the same composition as alum.

Only a small number of the salts of ekaboron should crystallize well.

The sulfate of scandium does not form distinct crystals, but the nitrate, the acetate and the formate crystallize well.

Supposed Characteristics of Ekaboron	Observed Characteristics of Scandium
Water should decompose the anhydrous chloride of ekaboron with release of HCl.	The crystallized chloride decomposes and sets free HCl when it is heated.
The oxide ought to be infusible, and it ought, after calcination, to dissolve in acids, although with difficulty.	The calcined oxide is an infusible powder, which dissolves in acids with difficulty.
The density of the oxide is about 3.5.	The density of the oxide is equal to 3.8.

Yttrium

→THE BLACK mineral from Ytterby started the mystery of the Rare Earths, which plagued analytical chemists for a century and a half. The earthy, powdery nature of the oxides is responsible for the name of this group of elements. The name "ytter-earth," formalized to "yttrium," was given to the first indication of a new element from the new Swedish mineral. It has been retained as the name of element 39, a lighter analogue of the Rare Earth elements.

The Rare Earth series is introduced by Lanthanum, element 57, from which the new name Lanthanide Series is derived. These elements will be described in the next section of this book, in chronological order, as one after another of them was identified.

The elements of Group III b, with their rather inert, colorless compounds, have never been favorites with chemists. They lack the dramatic qualities of the more alkaline elements on one side of them in the table, and the more acidic ones on the other. They also lack carbon's glamour, shared to some extent by its analogues, of building up chains of self-linked atoms into the "organic" type of compound. Yet they have their own individuality.

A New Mineral

Excerpt from the following:

VON EINER SCHWARTZEN, SCHWEREN STEINART *aus Ytterby Steinbruch in Rosslagen in Schweden. (On a black, hard mineral from Ytterby quarry in Rosslagen in Sweden). By Prof. J. Gadolin*. In Chemische Annalen (Crell) Vol. 1, Helmstadt (Germany) 1796.*

→THIS MINERAL, noteworthy on account of its unusual weight, was first discovered by Capt. Arrhenius in Ytterby quarry, ¼ mile from Warholm Castle, where a white feldspar is dug for the Stockholm porcelain factory. . . .

From its properties one finds that this earth agrees in many ways with alumina, but in other ways with lime, so that it is distinguished from both, even as much as from the other, already known earths. Therefore it seems to deserve a place among the elemental earths, because the tests so far made do not allow grouping with any others. At the present time I dare not claim such a new discovery, because my small supply of the black mineral does not allow me to carry out the research according to my wishes. Apart from that, I hesitate also for this reason, that much more knowledge would be gained if the several new earths, recently described by the analysts, could be decomposed into their elemental constituents, as then the number of the new simple earths will be still further increased.

A New Earth

Excerpt from the following:

FERNERE UNTERSUCHUNGEN DER SCHWARTZEN STEINART VON YTTERBY *und der in Derselben Gefundenen Eigenthümlichen Erde. (Further Investigation of the Black Mineral from Ytterby and the Peculiar Earth found in it.) By A. G. Ekeberg. In Chemische Annalen (Crell), Helmstadt (Germany), 1799.*

→PROF. GADOLIN, in the Transactions of the Royal Academy of Sciences (Stockholm) for the year 1794, second quarter, has described an investigation of a black mineral from the Ytterby quarries in Rosslagen, and at the same time the announcement of the chemical analysis by which he accomplished the discovery of a new and hitherto unknown earth. It seemed necessary to determine the properties of this earth, in order to decide upon its identity and its differences from those already known. Yet with the assurance which only older and more experienced analysts have, it was given a place as a true earth, without any reservation or more exact knowledge. Upon getting the opportunity, I have also subjected this material to analysis, and there seems to me no longer any doubt that it should have this place.

Captain Arrhenius, whose enthusiasm for science gave Prof. Gadolin the opportunity to investigate this material, is also the one who has put me in the way of being a collaborator in the discovery. Such a beautiful piece of the mineral was sent me

* The foregoing communication was accompanied by a letter to me, dated July 3, 1794: but both came first to my sight on the 26th of March of this year (1796), as I can vouch for truthfully. The most plausible explanation of this seems to be, that the letter was put in charge of a traveller on a journey, so that, perhaps through various circumstances, it may have lain overlooked for a long time. While lost, the paper has not been given the consideration for which it was prepared, so several explanations are due Prof. Klaproth's excellent contribution.—C.

by him that after breaking it up I could select little pieces free from feldspar for analysis. Since Prof. Gadolin did not have this advantage, the proportion of constituents in my determination must naturally be somewhat different from that given by him. For it is clear, that the included feldspar would increase the percentage of silica and alumina, at the expense of the other substances.

Upon a weighed sample of the mineral was poured 16 times as much pure muriatic acid, and the mixture was held at gentle ebullition until the soluble part was extracted, and the clay remained as a white, cheesy mass. After drying and ignition, this weighed 25 parts, and with soda gave a glass bead before the blowpipe, which remained clear upon cooling.

From the filtered solution, which appeared lemon yellow in the cold and bright green when warm, there was precipitated with caustic sal volatile (ammonium carbonate) a dirty-brownish earth. After this was separated by filtration, the liquid gave no precipitate with carbonated sal volatile, and yielded upon evaporation pure sal ammoniac (ammonium chloride). The reserved dirty precipitate, while still moist, was put into caustic potash solution and heated with it for some time, when the insoluble part was separated.

The potash-soluble part was saturated with nitric acid, which made it turbid, but it was cleared again by an excess of acid. It was then precipitated with carbonated sal volatile, and the alumina thus obtained weighed, after ignition, only 4½ parts.

What was left from the potash solution was dissolved in dilute sulfuric acid. After evaporation to dryness, the residue was strongly ignited, until it had taken on a red color through and through. Then it was digested with water and filtered, when a bright red iron ochre remained on the filter paper, which, after strong ignition, weighed 18 parts. The reason for this procedure is easy to see. The sulfuric acid solution contains the new earth, together with iron, and the question is, how can they be separated from each other? This, I thought, could most conveniently be done by ignition, because vitriol loses its acids thus, and, by analogy, it was to be expected that the compound of the earth with sulfuric acid would remain undecomposed, which indeed occurred.

The filtered solution was slowly evaporated, and it appeared that the compound of the earth with sulfuric acid could crystallize into beautiful crystals, of which the most conspicuous were nearly half as large as raisin seeds. As the solution shrank, the crystals became finer and the form less easily distinguished, until the last looked just like a powder. After all the salt was dissolved in water again, the earth was precipitated with carbonated sal volatile, ignited and weighed. It was found to amount to 47½ parts. . . .

From the experiments which I have made with the earth,

I will, to avoid diffuseness, omit those which agree with Prof. Gadolin's own, and merely state those which I regard as contributing to further description of the material.

All moistened and dissolved compounds of this earth with an acid have a very sweet taste, like solutions of lead, not so unpleasant but more sharp and astringent. Its compound with acetic acid is, in my opinion, fully as sweet as sugar of lead.
. . .

I find nothing to hinder me from believing that the properties and characteristics of this earth are just as well defined as those of any hitherto known; as proof I will enumerate several especially striking reactions by which this substance can be distinguished from others.

It is distinguished from barytes in that it gives a soluble salt with sulfuric acid, and cannot be made to crystallize with nitric and muriatic acids. From lime by its crystals with sulfuric and acetic acids. From magnesia in the same way, and from all three by this, that they are precipitated by caustic sal volatile. From alumina, in that it is not dissolved by caustic potash lye, and gives with acetic acid a salt stable in air. From silica, aside from its solubility in acids, because it can be dissolved again from the ignited carbonate in the wet as well as in the dry way. . . .

Its reaction with carbonic acid differentiates it from zircon, not to mention its taste and the crystals of its neutral salt. It cannot be confused with strontia, which forms a most difficultly soluble compound with sulfuric acid, and one capable of crystallization with nitric and muriatic acids. Also it does not correspond especially with *Australerde,* which can be dissolved in no acid except muriatic, and in that not without boiling. It thus takes its proper and deserved place in the system of neutral elements, as a simple and independent earth.

It must therefore be named, and it seems most fitting that it should be named from the place where it was first discovered, because neither the name of the discoverer nor that of the mineral are sufficiently short for forming a name for common speech. But it can be called Ytter-earth, in Latin *Yttria,* which is free from all ambiguity and confusion both in meaning and spelling. The mineral itself should no longer be called pitchstone, for that has an entirely different meaning, such substances dug up elsewhere are so named, but it should be called *Ytterstein.*

In regard to the opinions as to the use of the discovery of a new earth, I cannot quite agree with Prof. Gadolin, for Yttria has such clear and definite properties. By complicated and troublesome investigation it may be possible at another time to achieve much understanding and profit. Is baryta not indispensable now in manufacturing many substances, and necessary in analysis, and what need does it not fill in medicine! That Yttria, whose acid solutions have such a characteristic taste, may also find a use in medicine is perhaps not such an untruthful possibility.

What may be discovered through further research upon the nature of this earth and its behavior toward other bodies, I leave for the future to show.

Actinium

Excerpt from the following;
SUR UNE NOUVELLE MATIÈRE RADIOACTIVE. *(On a new radioactive material.) Note de M. A. Debierne, présentée par M. J. Violé. Comptes rendus, Vol. 129, 1899.*

➤ M. AND MME. CURIE have shown[1] that the emission of rays found in pitchblende proves to be not solely from the uranium contained in it, they have discovered the presence of two new radiant elements, polonium and radium, much more active than uranium.

Polonium acts like an element very much like bismuth, accompanying it in all its chemical reactions, but from which it may be separated slowly by repeated fractionations. Radium has all the chemical reactions of barium and it is also only by repeated fractionation that it is possible to observe a separation.

The individuality of these new elements, at first shown solely by their radio-activity, has been confirmed, for one of them, by observation of a distinct spectrum, made by M. Demarçay with radium prepared by M. and Mme. Curie. It seems therefore that the property of emitting such radiations can serve to discover and to characterize such chemical elements.

Upon the advice of M. and Mme. Curie, I investigated whether there were any other radiant ingredients in pitchblende, and my researches have been carried out chiefly upon those substances whose acid solutions are not precipitated by hydrogen sulfide, but are completely precipitated by ammonia or ammonium sulfhydrate.

The material which I used came from a plant for the refining of uranium minerals and was therefore almost completely free from uranium. The quantity of radiant products contained in this material appeared to be extremely slight, a first task consisted of organizing the treatment of a very great quantity of material, certainly many kilograms, and eliminating as completely as possible the radiant materials already known (polonium and radium).

The greater part of the product precipitated by ammonia was composed of oxides of iron and aluminum; but, besides these substances, I recognized the presence of a large number of others which were present in very small proportions. Thus I have been able to separate small quantities of zinc, manganese,

[1] Work done at the laboratory of chemistry and physics at the Sorbonne.

chromium, vanadium, uranium, titanium, niobium, and tantalum; the rare earths were also represented, and I have been able to determine lanthanum, didymium, cerium and yttrium.

The radio-activity, which existed in a slight degree in the crude mass of the group precipitable by ammonia, became concentrated at certain points according to the separations which were made.

I have thus ascertained that the portion containing titanium and its analogues shows the radio-activity to a very intense degree, and after a rather complicated treatment, the nature of which I shall come back to later, I have obtained a substance whose solutions show the principal analytical properties of titanium, but which emit extremely active rays.

The radio-activity of one fraction of this material has been determined roughly to be a *hundred thousand* times as great as that of uranium. Moreover, this material has chemical properties entirely different from those of radium and of polonium.

The radiations given off by this material are entirely comparable to those which have already been observed by M. and Mme. Curie for polonium and radium.

They give off a gas capable of discharging electrified bodies, they excite phosphorescence in barium platinocyanide and they leave an image on a photographic plate.

The new material nevertheless is different from radium in that it is not spontaneously luminescent: M. and Mme. Curie have in fact found that the compounds of radium, in the dark, emit a perfectly distinct glow.

By Transmutation, 1948

ACTINIUM was one of the first radioactive elements to be discovered, nearly 50 years ago, but it is still one of the least known. It occurs in nature in small amounts, and was discovered in 1899 by Andre Debierne in working over some of Mme. Curie's pitchblende residues. But Dr. French Hagemann of the Argonne National Laboratory in 1948 chose the method of transmutation rather than that of separation, and made his sample of actinium out of radium by irradiation.

Chemists working with the newly-made heavy elements beyond uranium are very much interested in learning more about actinium. They are quite strongly committed to the theory that elements heavier than radium, beginning with actinium, belong to a series, as yet only half discovered, which duplicate in most of its properties the series of rare earths introduced by lanthanum. Yet in setting up this hypothesis, they have to rely on the probable nature of an element about which almost nothing is known.

At the time of Debierne's discovery, chemical techniques were based on work with very much larger quantities of material than are used in the newer methods today. It was sufficient for the Argonne Laboratory group to take one gram of radium and transmute a part of it to get three-quarters of a milligram of actinium, enough for a whole series of actinium compounds including halogen compounds, a sulfide and a phosphate. They find that, like other Group III elements, actinium is precipitated by ammonia as a gelatinous mass.

Actinium 227, the only long-lived isotope of the element, occurs in nature and is characterized by beta emission with a small amount of alpha emission. Its chemical properties are so similar to those of lanthanum that they cannot be separated by ordinary methods. In two extant samples prepared by Mme. Curie, when actinium was first discovered, the radioactive element was carried by lanthanum and each sample contains only about one per cent actinium.

The modern experimenters, therefore, being anxious to get the pure element uncontaminated by others with similar properties, chose to make their sample by transmutation from a different element. Actinium can be obtained as a decay product of proto-actinium, but this is also an extremely rare substance in nature, and its colloidal chemical properties are reported by Dr. Seaborg to be "exasperating." The Argonne Laboratories group, instead, made their actinium by irradiating radium 227 in the atomic pile.

The Actinide Series

➤ RECOGNITION that the lanthanide series of elements is paralleled by another series of elements, whose atomic structure is like theirs, was slow in coming. Although the new "rare earth" series was foretold by Niels Bohr, the element with which it would begin was left in doubt, and chemists were misled about the nature of the heaviest elements, because little was known about them.

Not until the possibility of atomic fission of U 235 led to intensive study of the properties of uranium and thorium were some errors about these two elements cleared up.

Actinium had been recognized as a Group III element, following the unmistakable Group II characteristics of radium, but chemists believed that the rest of the heavy elements would follow the conventional pattern of the periodic table. They accordingly placed thorium in Group IV and uranium in Group VI, although they complained that their properties are not much like those of the lighter elements in those groups.

Protactinium was so scarce that its chemical properties were hardly known at all. It was assumed to be a Group V element, and chemists expected that element 93, if found, would correspond to the then unknown analogues of manganese.

Not until the synthesis of the man-made transuranian elements was accomplished was it possible to recognize that their properties correspond to those of the rare earths.

The Rare Earths

Lanthanide Series

ELEMENT	ELECTRON SHELLS
$_{58}$Ce	$= K_2L_8M_{18}N_{20}O_8P_2$
$_{59}$Pr	$= K_2L_8M_{18}N_{21}O_8P_2$
$_{60}$Nd	$= K_2L_8M_{18}N_{22}O_8P_2$
$_{61}$Pm	$= K_2L_8M_{18}N_{23}O_8P_2$
$_{62}$Sm	$= K_2L_8M_{18}N_{24}O_8P_2$
$_{63}$Eu	$= K_2L_8M_{18}N_{25}O_8P_2$
$_{64}$Gd	$= K_2L_8M_{18}N_{25}O_9P_2$
$_{65}$Tb	$= K_2L_8M_{18}N_{27}O_8P_2$
$_{66}$Dy	$= K_2L_8M_{18}N_{28}O_8P_2$
$_{67}$Ho	$= K_2L_8M_{18}N_{29}O_8P_2$
$_{68}$Er	$= K_2L_8M_{18}N_{30}O_8P_2$
$_{69}$Tm	$= K_2L_8M_{18}N_{31}O_8P_2$
$_{70}$Yb	$= K_2L_8M_{18}N_{32}O_8P_2$
$_{71}$Lu	$= K_2L_8M_{18}N_{32}O_9P_2$

➤ EIGHT years after Gadolin's discovery of a new "earth" in the black, hard mineral from Ytterby, another unknown substance was found in another Swedish mineral, this time from Bastnas. Several analytical chemists worked on the small samples sent them by Klaproth and by Berzelius, two leaders in mineral analysis.

The analysts were looking for the newly discovered yttrium, but their tests showed still another new substance, whose properties could not be reconciled with those of Gadolin's discovery. Berzelius and his associate, Hisinger, named the metal of the Bastnas mineral "cerium," from the recently found asteriod Ceres.

About 1827 Mosander, a pupil of Berzelius, made some experiments with cerium oxide which indicated that some other substance was present. Years of work followed, and Mosander became the first of a long list of chemists who suffered from frustration through trying to separate compounds of the "rare earths." How he succeeded, and how later chemists continued to find one element after another with the somewhat neutral and indeterminate properties of Group III elements is outlined here in quotations from the discoverers of the rare earths.

The names assigned to the various fractions into which the rare earth material was split up varied from time to time. New elements were announced, and abandoned. Analytical methods were refined and new techniques were developed to try to cope with the puzzle of the new elements. There were too many of them, their properties were too much alike, their atomic weights too close together. Reluctantly chemists were obliged to add a footnote to the periodic table to take care of the fourteen elements all seeming to crowd into one space in Group III.

It was long before the properties of the rare earth elements were sorted out, and many thought to be criteria of new elements were later found to be due to something quite different.

The most interesting point about the gradual discovery of the rare earths is the evolution of analytical methods during the 150 years since the discovery of the first mineral at Ytterby. Solution of the problem of separating these baffling materials did not come until neodymium and its close relatives began to appear in quantity among the uranium fission products.

Cerium

Klaproth

NEW EARTH. *Note in Phil. Mag. XIX, London, 1804.*
→ KLAPROTH has discovered a new earth in an ore which has hitherto been supposed to contain tungsten. He has given it the name of *ochroit* earth. It seems to form the connecting link between the earths and the metallic oxides. It produces, like yttria, a reddish-colored salt with sulfuric acid, and is precipitable by all the prussiates; but it differs from yttria in not forming sweet salts, in not being soluble in carbonate of ammonia (or but little so), and in acquiring, when ignited, a light brown color. It also differs from yttria by not being fusible either by borax or by phosphates, with which yttria fuses into a colorless transparent globule.

Hisinger

ON CERIUM, *a new metal found in a mineral substance of Bastnas in Sweden, called Tungsten, Described by W. d' Hisinger and J. B. Berzelius. In Phil. Mag. XX, London, 1805.*
→ THOUGH this substance was formerly tried by Scheele and d'Ellhuyar, under the name of wolfram, yet its considerable specific gravity determined us to subject it to further researches. Our object in particular was to find yttria, which, being unknown at the time when these chemists carried on

their labors, might have escaped their attention. Our suspicions were ill-founded; since, instead of an earth, we found in it, according to every appearance, a substance hitherto unknown, as will be seen by what follows:

The tungsten of Bastnas, which we call cerite, for reasons which will be hereafter mentioned, was found in the year 1750, in a copper mine called Bastnas, or Saint Gorans' Koppar-grufva, at Riddare-Hyttan, in Westmannia, of which it formed with asbestos the matrix; but after that time it was inclosed in quartz and mica, at a depth of seventeen toises.

Tungsten is almost always mechanically mixed with black amphibolite (hornblend), striated actinote, of a bright green color (schorl), with mica, sulfuretted copper, bismuth, and sulfuretted molybdena, as one may be more readily convinced by exposing it to the fire.

Cerite, properly so called, is transparent, of a flesh color, sometimes dark, sometimes bright, and rarely yellow. The stone in a mass, and in small specimens, is of an irregular form; its fracture is indeterminate, compact, and somewhat brilliant; the edges obtuse; its consistence is tenacious and strong; it strikes fire with difficulty, but it does not scratch glass; it is not susceptible of attraction by the magnet; but when it has been brought to a red heat in the fire, it loses its hardness and six or seven per cent of its weight. By this operation it becomes friable, and assumes a bright yellow color; it does not fuse alone. . . .

Heated by the blow-pipe with borax, it forms a glass globule, which, when warm, appears greenish, but colorless when it has cooled. When fused with carbonate of soda, in a platina spoon, it is not dissolved. . . .

Analysis of Cerium

To separate the yttria, which it was suspected to contain, it was reduced to a fine powder in a porphyry mortar, and pure concentrated nitric acid was then added to it. The acid was decomposed, and a considerable quantity of nitrous and carbonic gases was disengaged. The stony powder was several times treated with acid, until the insoluble residuum appeared white.

The solution, diluted with water, had a yellow color, which became greenish by ebullition, and then red;—when dried completely, it became yellowish white; but by attracting humidity it resumes its red color.

In alcohol it is entirely dissolved, and the solution, when slightly digested, deposits a considerable quantity of oxide of iron. It deposited also more oxide of iron during a rest of some days in a window. The solution decanted, being almost clear, was evaporated to dryness, and the salt calcined exhibited a powder of a brick color. Water was able to dissolve only the calcareous earth. . . .

Ammonia precipitated from the solution of the alcohol a white powder, which became yellowish in the air. It was a little soluble by carbonate of ammonia, and, by calcination, assumed a brick color. The sediment being separated, the carbonate of ammonia produced a white precipitate, which was pure carbonate of lime. The acetous salt then contained no yttria. The powder from which the calcareous earth had been separated, solved in muriatic acid, disengaging oxygenated muriatic acid gas, which indicated that it was a metallic oxide.

Was it oxide of manganese united with oxide of iron?

To ascertain this, we tried to develop the pure oxide from the manganese by means of the tartrite of potash, according to the method of Richter. In this manner we decomposed with tartrite of potash a solution of this substance in muriatic acid perfectly neutralized, and, after having well washed the white precipitate, we subjected it to slow calcination; but this produced only powder of a brick color.

To Obtain Oxide of Cerium

Dissolve pure cerite, not calcined, in nitro-muriatic acid, and, having saturated the clear solution with alkali, precipitate it by tartrite of potash. The precipitate, when well washed, calcined, and digested in vinegar, contains pure oxide of cerium. . . .

This oxide may appear under different degrees of oxidation. Alkalies precipitate from its solutions a white oxide, which in the air has a yellowish color, but which when perfectly dry becomes dark. When exposed to a strong heat, long continued, it assumes a dark brick color. The oxalate and acetate of cerium, when calcined in vessels not completely shut, give a white oxide, which on an open fire becomes of a brick color. It does not fuse alone.

These and the following circumstances have determined us to consider the substance found in cerite as the oxide of a metal hitherto unknown, to which we have given the name of *cerium,* from the planet Ceres discovered by Piazzi.

The Referee

ACCOUNT OF EXPERIMENTS *made on a mineral called Cerite, and on the particular substance which it contains, and which has been considered as a new metal. By M. Vauquelin, in Phil. Mag. XXII, London, 1805.*

→M. KLAPROTH wrote to me, about eight months ago, that he had discovered, in a mineral of Bastnas, in Sweden, a new earth to which he had given the name of *ochroit,* on account of the red color which it assumes by calcination. He even sent me in a letter a small specimen of this substance; and having discovered in it, by several trials, the presence of a considerable quantity of oxide of iron, I started some doubts, in a note which I read in the Institute, in regard to the color of that earth. I observed also in the same note, that this substance had as many metallic properties as earthy characters; but that the small quantity of it which I had in my possession did not allow me to give any decisive opinion on this subject.

Some time after, Messrs. Berzelius and Hisinger, having been informed, by their correspondents at Paris, of M. Klaproth's labor, wrote to me to claim a priority, stating that they had sent to M. Klaproth the specimens of that mineral which he had employed for his experiments, and that at the same time they had announced to him that they had found a new metal in it. I can give no opinion on this difference. I shall only observe, that the well known delicacy of M. Klaproth, and the high reputation he has justly acquired by his numerous and important discoveries, render it very improbable that he would appropriate to himself the discovery of another. M. Klaproth must, no doubt, have received from another quarter the mineral in question; and his labor was perhaps terminated before he acquired any information respecting that of the Swedish chemists. What seems to justify this opinion is, that they obtained results entirely different.

Everything, therefore, seems to show that M. Klaproth of Berlin, and Messrs. Berzelius and Hisinger of Stockholm, made experiments at the same time on the mineral without having any communication with each other; and that each may have had the honor of the discovery.

Lanthanum

Rumor

LATANIUM—*A new metal. Phil. Mag. 14 (3rd series), 1839.*
M. BERZELIUS, in a letter to M. Pelouze, dated the 22nd of February, states that M. Mosander, in submitting the cerite of Bastnas, in which cerium was met with twenty-five years ago, has discovered a new metal.

The oxide of cerium, separated from the mineral by the usual process, contains nearly two-fifths of its weight of the oxide of the new metal, merely altered by the presence of the cerium, and which, so to speak, is hidden by it. This consideration induced M. Mosander to give the new metal the name of *latane* or *lantan*.

It is prepared by calcining the nitrate of cerium, mixed with nitrate of latanium. The oxide of cerium loses its solubility in weak acids; and the oxide of latanium, which is a very strong base, may be separated by nitric acid, mixed with 100 parts of water.

Oxide of latanium is not reduced by potassium; but by the action of potassium on the chloride of latanium a gray metallic powder is obtained, which oxidizes in water with the evolution of hydrogen gas, and is converted into a white hydrate.

The sulphuret of latanium may be produced by heating the oxide strongly in the vapor of oxide [sulphuret?] of carbon. It is of a pale yellow color, decomposes water with the evolution of hydro-sulphuric acid, and is converted into a hydrate.

The oxide of latanium is of brick-red color, which does not appear to be owing to the presence of oxide of cerium. It is converted by hot water into a white hydrate, which restores the blue color of litmus reddened by an acid; it is rapidly dissolved even by very dilute acids; and when it is used in excess, it is converted into a subsalt. The salts have an astringent taste, without any mixture of sweetness; the crystals are usually of a rose-red color. The sulphate of potash does not precipitate them, unless they are mixed with salts of cerium. When digested in a solution of hydrochlorate of ammonia, the oxide of latanium dissolves, with the evolution of ammonia. The atomic weight of latanium is smaller than that assigned to cerium; that is to say, to a mixture of the two metals.

M. Berzelius has repeated and verified the experiments of M. Mosander.

Verification

ON THE NEW METALS, *Lanthanum and Didymium, which are associated with Cerium; and on Erbium and Terbium, new metals associated with Yttria. By Prof. C. G. Mosander.* *Phil. Mag. XXIII, 152, Oct. 1843.*

→ALTHOUGH in consequence of the imperfect nature of the results which were obtained from my researches on cerium and lanthanum I had no intention of making any communication on the subject on the present occasion, yet after hearing the interesting statement of Professor Scheerer, it appeared to me that it might be useful to make known more generally some particulars which arose during my labors, and principally because this advantage may result, that other chemists, after becoming acquainted with what I am about to state, may possibly be spared the loss of valuable time which might otherwise have been fruitlessly expended.

When sixteen years since I made some experiments upon cerium, several circumstances occurred which led me to the supposition that oxide of cerium was accompanied by some other oxide, which, however, I did not succeed in separating, and want of materials prevented me from then prosecuting the inquiry. A few years since, having procured a quantity of cerite and cerine, I prepared from thence the double salt of sulfate of the oxide of cerium with sulfate of potash, until the

* Communicated to the meeting of the Scandinavian Association at Stockholm, July 1842. Translated from the Swedish by Maj. North Ludlow Beamish, F.R.S., President of the Cork Scientific and Literary Society; and read before the Section of Chemistry and Mineralogy of the British Association, meeting at Cork, Aug. 18, 1843.

passing fluid gave no trace of precipitate with caustic ammonia or carbonate of soda. I believed that in this manner I could obtain a pure salt free from all foreign substances. The double salt was afterwards decomposed in the moist way with carbonate of soda, and with the carbonate of protoxide of cerium thus obtained, all the preparations have been made which will now be mentioned.

After a long examination of various salts of protoxide of cerium, I did not succeed in detecting a salt principally consisting of the supposed new oxide, the presence of which, however, appeared more and more probable in the course of the experiments.

As it was known that cerium gives two oxides, I considered it probable that if hydrate of protoxide of cerium mixed with water was exposed to the effect of chlorine, peroxide of cerium would be formed while the more electro-positive metallic oxide would be dissolved in the fluid, and it was in this manner that I succeeded to my satisfaction.

When the chlorine was introduced into the fluid, the appearance of the hydrate of protoxide of cerium began soon to change, the volume diminished, and a heavy, bright, yellow, or rather orange-yellow colored powder fell to the bottom. If, after the chlorine no longer appears to cause any change, the fluid is filtered, a colorless solution, with the strong odor of hypochlorous acid, is obtained, from which, with hydrate of potash in excess, a precipitate is deposited which, collected on a filter, is white, or approaching violet.

This precipitate begins soon, however, to grow yellow in contact with the air. If the precipitate be again mixed with water and chlorine introduced, the greater part is dissolved, while a new portion of the yellow-colored oxide is formed, and remains undissolved.

The filtered solution forms a precipitate again with caustic potash, which is treated as before with chlorine, and this is repeated five or six times, when finally, hydrate of potash precipitates from the solution an oxide which does not become in the least yellow by exposure to the air, and which, suspended in water, is completely dissolved by the introduction of chlorine without leaving a trace of undissolved yellow oxide.

It was to this oxide, not capable of being more oxidized either by the air or chlorine, that I gave the name oxide of Lanthanum, after the production of which, and a nearer acquaintance with its properties, another and simpler method was employed to obtain it.

The strong basic qualities of the new oxide afforded an easy means of separating it from oxide of cerium, by treating the red-brown oxide which is obtained when the so-called nitrate of protoxide of cerium is heated with nitric acid diluted with 75 to 100 parts of water. An acid thus diluted leaves the greater part of the red-brown oxide undissolved, and from the solution thus obtained the oxide of lanthanum was derived which was employed by me in the experiments that I made in the beginning of the year 1839.

Some of the results which I obtained unfortunately became known to the public. When we find the oxide of a body hitherto unknown, nothing, generally speaking, is easier than the determination of the qualities of the body, and I therefore expected to be able to give a complete account of my experiments in a very short time, but on this point I was much deceived.

Although at the end of the year 1839 I had already been fortunate enough to obtain oxide of lanthanum tolerably pure, it was not until the beginning of the following year that I was able, with any facility, to obtain a larger quantity of it; but, notwithstanding all my efforts, I have not yet succeeded in discovering any method of separating, with any degree of analytical accuracy, lanthanum from cerium, &c.

Oxide of lanthanum, as pure as I have hitherto been able to obtain it, possesses the following properties: It is of a light salmon color, or nearly white, but not in the least reddish or brown, and retains its appearance unchanged when heated either in open or closed vessels at a red or white heat: the slight color seems to proceed from a small remnant of some foreign substance. The oxide, although just previously ignited to a white heat, soon changes its appearance in water, becomes snow-white, more bulky, and after twenty-four hours in the ordinary temperature of the air, becomes changed to a hydrate easily suspended in water.

With boiling water this change takes place very quickly, and begins immediately; the newly heated oxide as well as the hydrate immediately restores the blue color to moist reddened litmus paper. Oxide of lanthanum is easily dissolved by acids even much diluted. Salts, when they are formed by the combination of the oxide of lanthanum with uncolored acids, are absolutely colorless, as well as the most concentrated solutions of the same. Salts of lanthanum have a sweet, slightly astringent taste, and the solution of them can be completely separated from oxide of lanthanum by the addition of sulfate of potash in sufficient quantity, because the double salt formed by sulfate of lanthanum and sulfate of potash is quite insoluble in a solution saturated with sulfate of potash.

The atomic weight of oxide of lanthanum, as it has hitherto appeared in most instances, has oscillated about 680, a number which, however, possesses no scientific value, when, as I have already remarked, an absolutely pure oxide has not yet been obtained.

Didymium

The oxide of lanthanum which was first obtained by me was of a brown color, but after having been heated to a white heat, became a dirty white; by heating in hydrogen it also lost its brown color, although a scarcely perceptible loss of weight arose therefrom; by heating in the air, the brown color returned.

This circumstance, together with several other phenomena which presented themselves during the exmaination of the properties of the oxide of lanthanum, caused me to presume that the oxide of lanthanum which had been obtained was still accompanied by some unknown oxides, and it was in the beginning of 1840 that I succeeded in freeing lanthanum from that very substance which caused the brown color. To the radical of this new oxide, I gave the name of Didymium (from the Greek word διδυμος whose plural διδυμοι signifies twins), because it was discovered in conjunction with oxide of lanthanum. It is the oxide of didymium that gives to the salts of lanthanum and cerium the amethyst color which is attributed to the salts; also the brown color which the oxides of the same metals assume when heated to a red heat in contact with the air.

Notwithstanding all possible care, I have not succeeded in obtaining the oxide in a state of purity; and I have only arrived so far as to ascertain that a constant compound with sulfuric acid can be produced by different means, but from the quantity of water of crystallization, and other circumstances, the conclusion may be drawn that the salt is really a double salt, although I cannot at present say whether the other accompanying oxide is oxide of lanthanum, or some other.

I must not omit to mention on this occasion that amongst the many other bodies which in the course of these researches I was obliged to examine, yttria also presented itself, and I have found this earth, free from foreign substances, is perfectly colorless, and gives perfectly colorless salts: that the amethyst color which the salts generally present comes from didymium, I will not, however, maintain.

Terbium and Erbium

Addendum, July 1843.

I published last summer a short notice of Yttria, concerning which earth the following facts subsequently discovered merit attention. When I stated on the former occasion that pure yttria, as well as the salts of that base with a colorless acid, are colorless, my experiments had only gone so far as to show that all the yttria which I could procure for examination might with ease be separated into two portions, the one a stronger and colorless base, the other a weaker, which, in proportion as it was free from yttria, acquired a more intense yellow color on being submitted to heat, and with acids gave salts of a reddish color.

I continued my examination during the following autumn and winter, and thereby was not only enabled to confirm the correctness of my former observations, but made the unexpected discovery that, as was the case with oxide of cerium, what chemists have hitherto considered as yttria, does not consist of one oxide only, but is for the most part to be regarded as a mixture of at least three, of which two appear to be new and hitherto unknown, all possessing the greater number of their chemical characters in common, for which reason chemists have so readily overlooked their real differences.

The characters which are peculiar to these oxides, and distinguish them from all others are, 1st that although powerful salt bases, all more so than glucina, they are insoluble in water and in caustic alkalies, but on the other hand soluble, even after having been exposed to a strong heat, in a boiling solution of carbonate of soda, although after a few days the greater part separates from its solution in the form of a double salt; 2ndly, that combined with carbonic acid, they are largely soluble in a cold solution of carbonate of ammonium, and that when such solution is saturated with them, a double salt of carbonate of ammonia and the above carbonates immediately begins to separate, and that in such quantity, that after a few hours very little oxide remains in solution; which explains the observations of several chemists, that, as they express themselves, yttria sometimes dissolves freely, sometimes scarcely at all, in carbonate of ammonia: further that the salts of these oxides have a sweet taste, and that the sulfates dissolve with more difficulty in warm than in cold water, without its following that they form double salts with sulfate of potash, which are insoluble in a saturated solution of the latter.

If the name of yttria be reserved for the strongest of these bases, and the next in order receives the name of oxide of terbium, while the weakest be called oxide of erbium, we find the following characteristic differences distinguishing the three substances:

The nitrate of yttria is extremely deliquescent, so much so that if a small portion of a solution of that salt be left for weeks in a warm place, the salt produced will not be free from humidity. The solution of nitrate of oxide of terbium, which is of a pale reddish color, soon evaporates, leaving a radiated crystalline mass, which does not change in air unless it be very damp. The crystals of sulfate of yttria are colorless, and remain clear and transparent for weeks in air at a temperature varying from 86° Fahr. to 158° Fahr., while a solution of sulfate of oxide of terbium yields by evaporation, at a low temperature, a salt which immediately effloresces to a white powder.

Oxide of terbium, the salts of which are of a reddish color, appears, when pure, to be devoid of color, like yttria. Oxide of erbium differs from the two former in its property of becoming of a dark orange-yellow color when heated in contact with air, which color it is again deprived of, with a trifling loss of weight, by heating it in hydrogen gas; and it is to the presence of oxide of erbium that yttria owes its yellow color, when prepared as hitherto directed: and it is moreover probable, that in all those cases where a colorless yttria has been supposed to have been obtained, the presumed yttria has consisted for the most part of glucina, at least before it was known how to separate the last earth completely. . . .

Ytterbium

On Ytterbine, *a New Earth Contained in Gadolinite. Note by M. C. Marignac in Comptes rendus, Vol. 87, Paris, 1878.* ➤As a result of the researches which I have made upon the earths from gadolinite, researches which had for their object and which have for their result the confirmation of observations by M. Delafontaine upon the existence of terbine and of a new base belonging to the same group, to which he gave the name *philippine,* I have obtained a few grams of an earth presenting all the characteristics which belong to erbine, following the classic work of MM. Bahr and Bunsen and of MM. Cleve and Hoglund.

I ought to state however that the process by which I separated it from the other earths of gadolinite is not absolutely identical with that which those chemists used. Bunsen's process consists of heating the mixed nitrates until red vapor appears, redissolving in boiling water and separating out the nitrite rich in erbine which precipitates in small needle-shaped crystals upon cooling the solution. As for me, I was able to carry the decomposition of the nitrates much further, up to the moment that the mass became sticky. Upon treating the mass with boiling water, there remains an insoluble residue in which the erbine is concentrated. By one or the other of these processes, repeated a very great number of times, we end by obtaining an earth of a pure rose color, which is erbine.

In my first researches, I stopped the treatment as soon as I arrived at a rose colored earth whose equivalent weight, lying between 128 and 129,* corresponded to that which has been assigned to erbine.

* Since the atomic weights of the rare earths are now known to lie between 140 and 175, it is evident that there was considerable mixture in these samples with lighter elements, probably yttrium and scandium. The oxide is of the formula R_2O_3, not RO, which also confused the results.—Editor's Note.

Unconfirmed Elements

Date	Name	Discoverer	Decision
1811	Junonium	T. Thomson	error
1818	Vestium	L. W. Gilbert	unverified
1851	Donarium	C. Bergmann	mixture
1862	Wasmium	J. F. Bahr	mixture
1878	Mosandium	J. L. Smith	mixture
1878	Philippium	M. Delafontaine	mixture
1878	Decipium	M. Delafontaine	mixture
1884	Rogerium	J. L. Smith	mixture
1886	Austrium	E. Linnemann	impure gallium
1887	Russium	K. von Chrustchoff	mixture
1892	Masrium	H. D. Richmond	unverified
1894	Demonium	H. E. Rowland	dysprosium
1896	Damarium	K. Lauer and P. Antsch	unverified
1896	Lucium	P. Barrière	mixture
1896	Kosmium	B. Kosmann	mixture
1898	Monium	W. Crookes	victorium
1899	Victorium	W. Crookes	mixture
1901	Euxenium	K. A. Hotmann	unverified
1904	Carolinium	C. Baskerville	unverified
1904	Berzelium	C. Baskerville	unverified
1905	Incognitum	W. Crookes	terbium-gadolinium
1905	Ionium	W. Crookes	terbium-gadolinium
1907	Aldebaranium	C. A. von Welsbach	neoytterbium
1907	Cassiopeium	C. A. von Welsbach	lutecium
1911	Celtium	G. Urbain	lutecium
1916	Denebium	J. M. Eder	unconfirmed
1916	Dubhium	J. M. Eder	unconfirmed
1917	Eurosamarium	J. M. Eder	unconfirmed
1920	Welsium	J. M. Eder	unconfirmed

To the above list should now be added the four elements recently replaced in the Periodic Table:—

1925	Masurium	Noddack, Tacke, Berg	replaced by technetium
1926	Illinium	Hopkins, Yntema, Harris	replaced by promethium
1929	Virginium	Allison	replaced by francium
1931	Alabamine	Allison	replaced by astatine

More recently, I have again taken up the products thus obtained, as I wished to assure myself whether, by continuing these same operations, I should obtain any further increase in the equivalent weight. Instead, I observed a fact which surprised me very much.

Whereas, in the first part of my work, the gradual increase of the equivalent weight corresponds to a deepening in intensity of the rose color and of the absorption bands characteristic of erbine, there came a time when, the equivalent weight continuing to increase slowly, the rose color and the absorption line diminished quite rapidly, so much so that the last product obtained was perfectly white, its salts colorless, and no longer giving the absorption lines.

The last three products obtained gave the equivalent weights 130.4, 130.6 and 130.8. The first two still showed a sensible rose color, especially in the oxalate and sulphate crystals. The number 131 can be set approximately as the limit of equivalent weight which may be reached, if one can operate upon a sufficient quantity of material to carry this method of purification far enough.

It is evident from this that the earth which I extracted from gadolinite, and which I believed to be erbine, was only a mixture of two distinct oxides. One, a pure rose color presenting a very characteristic absorption spectrum, ought to keep the name *erbine*, since these are the characteristics which have been considered as more distinctive of that base. The other is a new base, belonging to the same group, and for it I propose the name *ytterbine*, which will recall its presence in the mineral from Ytterby, and its similarity to yttria, on the one hand, by its lack of color, to erbine, on the other, by the magnitude of its equivalent weight, with both of them by the whole of its properties. . . .

Thulium and Holmium

ON TWO NEW ELEMENTS IN ERBINE, *Note by M.P.T. Cleve in Comptes rendus, Paris, Vol. 88, 1879.*

→ TOWARD the end of last year, M. Marignac discovered in erbine, till then considered an oxide of a single metal erbium, the oxide of a new metal, ytterbine, very strongly characterized. A short time afterward, M. Nilson found in erbine another oxide, scandine, whose salts are colorless like those of ytterbine. The substance which gives to the salts of erbine the red color and their beautiful absorption spectra, that is to say, the true erbine, is still unknown. I proposed to extract from the old erbine its coloring principle. I had at my disposal a considerable quantity of material almost entirely free from ytterbine; M. Nilson very kindly gave me his precious residues from the extraction of scandine and ytterbine: nevertheless I found it absolutely impossible to obtain a red oxide of constant molecular weight, even after hundreds of decompositions.

I have been driven, since then, to postulate the presence of still another unknown new oxide, so I asked M. Thalen to examine the absorption spectrum of the fraction which I regard as most pure in erbine, and at the same time to compare that spectrum with spectra of residues rich in ytterbine and yttria. Some absorption bands in the last fractions suggested the idea that the color of erbine is due to the presence of three oxides in the absorption spectra. I therefore combined the redder fractions, of molecular weight 126 to 127 (RO), and submitted them to a long series of decompositions, treating one fraction (A) for ytterbine, another (B) for yttria, and a third intermediate between them in which the true erbine ought to become concentrated. At the same time, I tried to concentrate the coloring matter in the residues rich in ytterbine (A) and in yttria (B). When I had pushed the decompositions until obliged to stop for lack of material, I sent the five fractions for examination by M. Thalen, who had the kindness to study them with great care. . . .

We see then that the (absorption) band x pertains to fractions situated near ytterbine, and that it does not exist in the fractions which derive from yttrium. But it is just the opposite with bands y and z; in fact, these bands, which lack everything found in the residues of ytterbine, appear more and more pure, in proportion as they approach yttrium.

It appears from these researches that the spectrum of the old erbine ought to be attributed to three distinct oxides. In fact, the color of the solutions of the diverse fractions is sensibly different. Thus the fractions treated for ytterbine are colored rose with a tint of violet, the fractions treated for yttria have an orange tint. Although I have a considerable quantity of the mixture of these three oxides, I am convinced that it will be useless to continue these researches until I am able to get still more.

As for the radical of the oxide occurring between ytterbine and erbine, which is characterized by the band x in the red part of the spectrum, I propose the name thulium, derived from Thule, the earliest name of Scandinavia. The atomic weight of the metal Tm ought to be about 113 (its oxide being RO); at least, its oxide is concentrated in the fractions which have the molecular weight 129.*

The true erbium, to which the common band should be attributed, probably has an atomic weight of 110 to 111. Its oxide is of a clear rose color.

The third metal, characterized by the bands y and z, which is found between erbine and terbine, ought to have an atomic

* See footnote, page 76.

weight lower than 108. Its oxide appears to be yellow; at least, all the fractions of molecular weight lower than 126 are more or less yellow. I propose for this metal the name of holmium, Ho, derived from the latinized name of Stockholm, in whose vicinity occur so many minerals rich in yttria.

It remains to tender M. Thalen my lively appreciation of the trouble which he has taken with all these researches.

Samarium

NEW SPECTRUM RAYS. *Observed in material extracted from Samarskite. Note by Lecoq de Boisbaudran, Comptes rendus, Vol. 88, 1879.*

➤IN EXAMINING with the spectroscope, both by absorption and by means of the electric spark, the products of my work upon the mixture of earths from samarskite (rich in didymium), I observed lines or bands not related to any formerly known body and not corresponding to the descriptions of spectrum lines of earths recently announced by Messrs. Delafontaine, L. Smith, Soret and de Marignac.

The new lines of emission and those of absorption appear to correspond (at least the principal ones) to a single substance, for they follow similar variations of intensity in the series of products obtained by fractional crystallization.

Emission Spectrum—It is composed especially of four bands shaded toward the left, formed of narrow lines of which the strongest is the most refrangible and constitutes the right-hand border of the band. . . .

Absorption Spectrum—It has two strong bands in the blue and many lines of less importance in the green. . . .

These two strong blue bands are seen very easily, either by gas light or by that of the sun.

The metal which gives rise to these new spectra is precipitated in the state of the double potassium sulfate, at the same time as didymium; its simple sulfate is a little less soluble than that of didymium; its oxalate precipitates before that of didymium; finally, ammonia separates first the oxide of the new substance, then didymium oxide. All these reactions have to be repeated a great number of times if we wish to get a complete separation. . . .

Awaiting further verification, my two blue absorption bands and my four emission bands seem therefore to indicate the existence of a substance hitherto unknown.

(The further verification awarded de Boisbaudran the right to name the element Samarium, from the mineral in which he found it.)

Gadolinium

On the Earths of Samarskite. *Note from M. C. Marignac, Comptes rendus, Vol. 90, 1880.*

→For two years I have conducted a series of researches upon the earths of American samarskite. I have forced myself to follow a completely systematic course, which may be very long, but with the help of it I hope, if I can continue it to its completion, to determine the presence of all the bases of this group which enter, to any notable proportion, into the composition of this mineral.

After having extracted the crude earths by the usual procedures, I have separated them first into several fractions by successive decomposition of their nitrates by heat. Each of these will soon be analyzed in its turn by other methods.

For the present I have concerned myself only with the portion of these earths whose nitrates decompose last. This is the part richest in yttrium, it is the part also in which is concentrated almost all the didymium. On the other hand, one is sure of not finding here any of the earths whose nitrates are decomposed easily (erbium, ytterbium, scandium, etc.).

In order to separate the different earths which are found here, I have had recourse to their difference in solubility in a saturated solution of potassium sulfate. But even though they show very great differences in response to this treatment, they affect each other reciprocally to such an extent that it is only after such treatments are repeated hundreds of times that one begins to make an approximate separation.

Since the beginning of this work, it has been established as a rule that, going from the most soluble to the least soluble, they show the following modifications.

First, from a pale yellow color and an equivalent weight near that of yttrium, they become colored more and more orange-yellow, while at the same time the weight increases. The coloration reaches its maximum for those products whose weight is between 113 and 118, then it diminishes as the weight continues to increase up to about 120. After that time the solubility in potassium sulfate decreases very rapidly, while the yellow coloration disappears and the equivalent weight decreases slowly, approaching that of the oxide of didymium, yet remaining a little way from it.

In accordance with these preliminary observations, I have divided my earths into four portions:

1st. Earths soluble in less than 100 parts of potassium sulfate, whose weight is less than 119*;

2nd. Earths soluble in 100-200 parts potassium sulfate, whose weight varies from 119 to 120;

* See footnote, page 76.

3rd. Earths very slightly soluble in potassium sulfate, weight ranging between 119 and 115;

4th. Earth practically insoluble. This is oxide of didymium, but holding very strongly a certain quantity of the preceding earths. I have pushed the extraction of these to the point where the solution is saturated with potassium sulfate, where didymium-potassium sulfate begins to be formed, retaining no more than 1/40,000 of the earth. It is unfortunate that the oxide of didymium is far from being completely freed from these earths.

Let us take again, successively, the first three groups.

I. *Earths soluble in less than 100 parts of potassium sulfate*. Upon continuing to give this the same treatment, it can be shown that the greater part dissolves in less than 30 parts of the solution. The rest owes its lessened solubility not only to the presence of a certain quantity of earths of the following groups, but also to the fact that they are redissolved by the repeated operations.

As for the more soluble earths, treatment with potassium sulfate is not sufficient to separate them, so this is accomplished at this point by using the difference in solubility of their formates. I have satisfied myself by this treatment that this group contains but two earths now known, yttria and terbine.

II. *Earths soluble in 100 to 200 parts of potassium sulfate*. If we continue to use the same method of concentration, separating the more soluble parts, rich in terbine, from the less soluble, which contain the earths belonging to the following group, we see the equivalent weight rise again, but very slowly. I have not been able to pass the maximum of 120.5.

The earth thus obtained is soluble in 100 to 150 parts of potassium sulfate solution. Its color, a rather pale orange, is perhaps due to a small quantity of terbine which I have not been able to eliminate completely. The salts and the solutions of this base are colorless; they do not show an absorption spectrum; we can distinguish only some traces of the lines of decipium and didymium. For the rest, all that I have seen of these salts do not differ in any way from those of the other earths or the yttrium group.

The fact that a maximum appears in the equivalent weight of this earth between the two neighboring groups proves incontestably its existence as a distinct entity. It cannot be confused with any of those which have been distinguished up to now. Its weak coloration, supposing this really to belong to it, and the absence of an absorption spectrum, do not permit us to put it with yttria and ytterbine. Its high equivalent weight removes it completely from the first, it differs from the second by a much greater basicity. Its nitrate is more resistant to decomposition by heat than is that of terbium, which is, itself,

decomposed with much greater difficulty than is that of ytterbium.

I shall designate this earth provisionally as Yα; It will be
time to give it a name when we can obtain it in the pure state,
and in sufficient quantity to make a study of its salts. Perhaps
it will be found to be identical with that of which M. Delafontaine, in a recent note, says: "I am examining also another
base from samarskite, which seems to resemble ytterbine very
closely."

III. *Earths very slightly soluble in potassium sulfate*. By following the application to these earths of the same method of
separation, we establish there the presence of (1) a little terbine and a notable quantity of the preceding Yα, which is
eliminated, but never completely, by rejecting all the parts
more soluble in potassium sulfate; (2) oxide of didymium
which may be separated, but incompletely also, by rejecting
the parts less soluble in potassium sulfate, or by fractionating
the products by partial decomposition of their nitrates by heat
or by successive precipitation with ammonia, basing this on the
greater basicity of this oxide; and (3) finally, an earth which
demands more than 2000 parts of potassium sulfate to dissolve it, which is almost colorless, showing no more than a
slight salmon tint, and which I have provisionally designated
as Yβ.

Its equivalent weight has dropped to 115.6; the very small
quantity of didymium which it retains (about 3 to 5 parts per
100) cannot influence this weight very much. I consider this,
rather, a maximum, by reason of the presence of the preceding earth.

But the most essential characteristic of this earth consists of
its absorption spectrum. Its solutions show, in fact, in their
spectrum, particularly in the blue and the violet, lines of extreme intensity. According to my observations, complemented
by those which M. Soret has been kind enough to make, these
lines correspond exactly with those which M. Delafontaine has
indicated as characteristic of his decipium, and still better with
the very detailed and precise description which M. Lecoq de
Boisbaudran has given, which he attributes to the oxide of a
new metal which he has designated by the name of *samarium*.

It is impossible not to admit that these three earths are
identical, at least as to the nature of the principle which com-
prises the greater part of them and determines their absorption spectrum. It would be difficult, besides, to understand how
it could be otherwise, since all three of them have been extracted from the same mineral by the same process.

So I would have no hesitation to call this earth by the name
decipium, for it seems natural to me to preserve the name
which was given it by the first author of its discovery, if only
it did not present, compared to decipium as described by M.

Delafontaine in his most recent Notice, two important differences which it is impossible for me to account for.

These differences consist in the pale yellow coloration, of the solutions and of the salts of my earth Yβ, while decipium formed colorless salts, and especially in the enormous difference in equivalent weight, which was at least equal to 130 for decipium, while I have found only 115.6 for my earth and I consider even that number a maximum.

These divergences can only be explained by further researches which I am not at the moment able to pursue, not having a sufficient quantity of material for them.

Summing up, the principal part of the earths from samarskite is composed of yttria, which is the main element, terbine, a new earth Yα, and a small quantity of oxide of didymium and of an earth which, if it is not pure decipium, is at least in large part composed of it.

(Decipium proved to be a mixture of other rare earths).

Gadolinium Named

M. MARIGNAC'S Y_a *is definitely named Gadolinium. Note from M. Lecoq de Boisbaudran. Comptes rendus, Vol. 102, 1886.*

➤IN THE COURSE of correspondence in which I have recently had the honor of taking part with M. de Marignac, I have taken the liberty of calling the attention of that illustrious chemist to the advantage it would be for those who work with rare earths, to see Y_a at last receive a definitive name from the author of its discovery. This interesting substance Y_a has been studied so well for a long time, and its spectrum shows such clear characteristics, that there can no longer be any doubt as to its individuality.

M. de Marignac has had the kindness to entrust to me the announcement to the Academy that he has chosen the name *gadolinium* (symbol Gd) for the metal of Y_a.

The drawing of the spectrum of Gd_2Cl_6, which I have the honor to place before the Academy, will without doubt interest the scientists who are concerned with the chemistry of minerals.

Praseodymium and Neodymium

THE SPLITTING OF DIDYMIUM *into its elements. By Dr. Carl Auer v. Welsbach. Monatshefte fur Chemie, Vol. VI, Vienna, 1885.*

➤THE END results of my researches on the group of metals of the rare earths, so far as they touch upon territory unknown or little known to science, I am treating in a series of separate publications, in order to bring together more easily the more interesting parts of this work.

A new separation technique, fractional crystallization of the ammonium double nitrates of lanthanum and didymium in strong saltpeter solution, in which these substances behave very differently, makes it possible not only to separate lanthanum completely from didymium in a few operations and obtain it practically pure for the first time, by which any desired quantity may be worked over with almost the same amount of trouble, but also to separate didymium itself into its specific components. After repetition many hundred times of the separation procedure the separated elements remained in abundant quantity and in the pure state.

The absorption spectra of the compounds of these elements are part of that hitherto considered as the characteristic absorption spectrum of didymium. When these elements are combined in the proper percentage, both the color of the solution and the original spectrum of didymium appear again unaltered.

The spectrum of didymium is indeed in the true sense the sum of the absorption spectra of the new elements.

The emission spectrum characteristic of didymium belongs to a single substance, all of whose intense absorption bands coincide with the lines of the incandescent earth.

The spark spectra of the new elements are brilliant and these similarly are to some extent part of the spark spectrum of didymium.

The compounds of the two new elements, now prepared pure, are of different colors. Those of the first, the one standing next to lanthanum, are a pure and intense leek-green, those of the latter, the ones standing farther from lanthanum, are practically pure rose or amethyst color.

The latter element makes up the chief part of the "decomposition elements" of didymium.

The methods employed in this work for production, determination of spectrum, etc., will be found in brief in my paper submitted to the Academy of Sciences, "Contributions to Spectrum Analysis."

Since now the true splitting of didymium into several elements has been realized, I propose not to strike out the name didymium completely and suggest, for the first element, in accordance with the green color of its salts and its derivation, the name: Praseodymium with the symbol Pr, and for the second, as the "new didymium," the name: Neodymium with the symbol Nd.

From the atomic weight determination, which was carried out in every detail according to Bunsen, the provisional weight for praseodymium works out at 143.6, for neodymium as

140.8, from which the corresponding oxide gives the general formula M_2O_3.

The properties exhibited by the two elements are sufficient to clarify many very widely contradictory results of chemical investigation hitherto shown by didymium.

Dysprosium

HOLMIUM (or Earth X according to M. Soret) contains at least two metallic radicals. Note by M. Lecoq de Boisbaudran. Comptes rendus, Vol. 102, 1886.

➤ IN OCTOBER 1878, M. Delafontaine announced a new earth, philippine, and attributed to it the strong absorption band placed at about 164.25 of my scale (λ=451.4), a band which was included in the spectrum of the old erbine.

At the beginning of 1880, M. Delafontaine recognized that the band 451.5 is due to the same substance as the other lines considered by M. Soret and by M. Cleve as characteristic of holmium. M. Delafontaine added that this holmium was identical with his philippium; he stated in particular that it was not possible to admit that the band 451.5 was proved due to the same entity as bands 640.4 and 536.3.

Finally, in August 1880 and September 1880, M. Soret replied that M. Delafontaine had given up his old idea of the identity of holmium and philippium, after having stated that this last substance does not give a visible absorption spectrum, and that the bands which were at first attributed to it really belong to holmium.

There result from this short historical summary these questions:— 1st. Whether M. Delafontaine's philippine has no visible absorption spectrum. 2nd. Whether all the lines in the following table (compiled by M. Soret) are actually regarded as belonging to a single element, holmium.

Visible spectrum of Earth X, or holmium, after M. Soret.

804 Very strong
753 Weak
604.4 ⎤
536.3 ⎬ Very characteristic
485.5 ⎦
474.5 Very weak and nebulous
453 to 449
430 Doubtful
414.5
389 to 387

I have succeeded meanwhile, by means of many hundred fractionations by means of ammonia and potassium sulfate, in obtaining, in one part, earths showing more strongly 753 and 451.5 in the complete absence of 640.4 and 536.3 and, in the other part, earths giving 753 and 451.5 much more feebly, while 640.4 and 536.3 appear very clearly.

The oxide hitherto called *holmine* is therefore not homogeneous and is composed of *at least* two radicals. As the lines 640.4 and 536.3 are pre-eminently those which served M. Soret and M. Cleve in discovering the presence of a new element in the old erbine, I propose to preserve the name *holmium* for the element giving rise to those lines and to give the name *dysprosium*[1] (symbol Dy) to the metal which gives the lines 753 and 451.5.

A study still has to be made to assure ourselves that 640.4 and 536.3 are really due to the same earth, and the same for 753 and 451.5.

As for the other bands contained in the above table, it will be necessary to classify them and to see if it is possible to divide all of them between the spectra of Ho and Dy.

In fractionation with potassium sulfate and alcohol, the first precipitates contain mostly terbine, then come dysprosine, holmine and then erbine.

Europium

On a New Element, Europium. *Note by Eugene Demarçay, presented by Henri Moissan, Comptes rendus Vol. 132, 1901.*

➤ In 1885 M. Crookes, in his beautiful researches on electric fluorescence in a vacuum, reported a band which he attributed to samarium and which, because of its disappearance in the presence of calcium and of some other peculiarities, he called the *anomalous line*. Later he distinguished it with a number of other bands as characterizing apparently some meta-element. He called S delta the hypothetical meta-element corresponding to the anomalous line. M. Lecoq de Boisbaudran, in the course of his important researches on phosphorescence, confirmed the announcements of M. Crookes upon the anomalous line.

In 1892, M. de Boisbaudran described a spectrum of three brilliant blue lines, discovered in the spark spectrum of samarium. These three lines could be strengthened by suitable fractionation. From this he concluded that they correspond to a particular element Z epsilon. At the same time he turned his attention to a particular band of the reversal spectrum of samarium which seemed to correspond to the anomalous line and was considerably strengthened in nitric acid

[1] The name is derived from Greek roots, meaning "hard to communicate with"—Ed.

solution. M. de Boisbaudran, without stopping for entirely precise conclusions, was inclined to believe it characteristic of a particular element Z zeta.

In 1896, I announced the presence of an element intermediate between gadolinium and samarium, characterized by various strong violet and ultra-violet lines. In 1900, I showed that this new element was identical with Z epsilon of M. Lecoq de Boisbaudran, that it was similar to the material to which the anomalous line of M. Crookes was due, the reversal line Z zeta, various other reversal lines not yet described, and, further, a special absorption spectrum unknown until that time. I added that it had not been possible for me to continue the fractionation long enough to affirm positively that all these properties correspond to the same substance. Since then, I have been able, following a considerable number of fractionations of magnesium nitrate, to accumulate a greater quantity of this scarcely abundant element, to fractionate it in turn and to report finally that these different characteristics: line spectrum, spectrum of reversal, absorption, electric fluorescence of the sulfate in vacuum (anomalous line) with calcium or gadolinium sulfate, accompany one another very constantly, remain sensibly proportional and that they evidently characterize the same element.

The apparently contradictory results of MM. Crookes and Boisbaudran are due, I think, to the varying proportion of Sigma-Z epsilon contained in their material and to the fact that calcium and gadolinium reinforce the spectrum of samarium more than of the other.

I propose for the new element the name europium, with the symbol Eu = 151 (approximately).

Lutetium

A NEW ELEMENT: LUTECIUM, resulting from the division of Marignac's ytterbium. Note by G. Urbain, presented by A Haller, Comptes rendus, Vol. 145, 1907.

→ IN THE SEPARATION of the elements of the yttrium group, I have always observed that ytterbium gives the most soluble salts. The method which seems to me the most practical for obtaining this substance, free from yttrium, erbium and thulium, is crystallization of the nitrates. I have obtained in 1905 by this method about 50 grams of raw ytterbium corresponding to the description given by Marignac.

I shall publish in summary form in this preliminary Note the researches which I have been pursuing constantly since that time.

One must always analyze the sulfates of such products to

determine the atomic weight of ytterbium. It seemed to me
necessary to submit ytterbium to systematic fractionation to
assure myself of the constancy of its atomic weight and its
characteristic spectra.

For this purpose, I subjected the nitrates to new fractional
crystallizations in nitric acid of density 1.3. I thus obtained,
after a very laborious task of fractionation, carried through 22
consecutive fractions, a series of products which I first examined from the point of view of absorption. The first fractions, numbered from 9 to 16, showed clearly those absorption bands which, *alone,* actually define thulium. I eliminated
those fractions. The other fractions which could be considered as those of pure ytterbium were changed into sulfates
and analyzed.

Far from being constant, the atomic weights varied, increasing progressively from 169.9 for fraction 17 to 173.8 for the
last fraction, No. 31. One such considerable variation is sufficient to establish the complexity of the real ytterbium.

I found thorium at the tail of my fractionations. By the
very efficacious method of MM. Wyrouboff and Verneuil (action of hydrogen peroxide on a neutral solution of the
nitrates), I have been able to separate from my earths of the
highest atomic weight about one five-thousandth part of thorium, which could not have any influence on my measurements.

By the method of arc spectra I have not been able to show
the presence of impurities in my products thus purified, and
it was unquestionable that my ytterbine was indeed a mixture
of several constituents.

By photographing upon the same plate, one below the
other, the arc spectra of the extreme products of the fractionation, I found in the spectrum of the last fraction (No.
31) numerous lines, for the most part strong, which could
not be found in the fraction at the head (No. 17), or which
appeared only very feebly. On the other hand, fraction 17
showed some lines of little intensity, absent in fraction 31
and probably attributable to thulium. Independently of these
lines, the two spectra showed a great number of lines in common with intensities of the same order. These lines are those
which characterize the principal amount of the material in
the beginning whose impurities (thulium and the new element) have accumulated, the one at the head and the other
at the tail, of my fractionation.

(*A detailed study of the various spectral lines follows*).

Within the limits between which my measurements were
made, these 34 lines constitute the relatively complete spark
spectrum of the new element.

None of these lines is attributable to scandium, to thorium,
to erbium, to thulium, to ytterbium, or to any ordinary element, nor to any rare earth except the old ytterbium.

I propose for this new element the name of *lutecium,* Lu,
derived from the ancient name of Paris.

*(The official spelling of the name of this element has re-
cently been changed to Lutetium, to correspond to similar
names of other elements—Editor's note.)*

Promethium

THE CHEMICAL IDENTIFICATION *of radioisotopes of Neodymium and Element 61. By J. A. Marinsky, L. E. Glendenin
and C. D. Coryell, in Journal of the American Chemical Society, 69:11 (1947).*

➤ IN THE COMPREHENSIVE studies of the radioactive species
produced in the fission of uranium it has been found that over
thirty are members of the rare earth family (isotopes of
yttrium and the group lanthanum through europium). The
chemical and physical identification of these was an important
part of the research program of the Manhattan Project.
Standard oxidative separations and fractional precipitations
and the use of radiochemical methods based on chain relations
served to distinguish the activities of yttrium, lanthanum,
cerium, and some of praseodymium, and those of samarium
and europium. The characterization of the sequence praseodymium, neodymium, and element 61 presented very difficult
problems that were solved only with the intensification of
ion exchange methods originally developed by Boyd and co-
workers and applied to the rare earth field by Cohn and
co-workers. In this paper is reported the successful separation
of these three elements, the first to have been achieved with
radioisotopes of neodymium and of element 61.

Earlier work on the Manhattan Project had revealed the
presence of two unidentified fission products in the rare earth
region. A soft beta emitting activity of about 4y half-life was
discovered by Ballou and independently by Goldschmidt and
Morgan. This activity was later studied by Seiler and Wins-
berg who set the half-life at about 3.7y. These investigators
considered the activity to be an isotope of praseodymium,
neodymium, or element 61 on the basis of detailed qualitative
chemical separations between lanthanum and praseodymium.
Another unidentified rare earth activity was later discovered
by Davies through its characteristic gamma radiations. This
was confirmed by Hume and Martens who determined its half-
life as about 11d and showed that the activity was not cerium.
We have been able to identify these two activities as isotopes
of element 61 and of neodymium, respectively, both of mass
number 147. In addition the 47h 61^{149} has been identified among the fission products. All three of these activities,

together with a previously unidentified 1.7h isotope of neodymium, are also produced as the result of the activation of neodymium with slow neutrons.

Chemical Identification

The 11d activity was first subjected to standard qualitative separations in order to limit the identification problem to a definite group of rare earth elements. Separations by carbonate digestion definitely eliminated yttrium and all rare earth elements of atomic number greater than 61. Oxidative fusion with sodium nitrate demonstrated that the activity was not an isotope of lanthanum and must therefore be identified with praseodymium, neodymium or element 61. Finally, the activity was limited to an isotope of neodymium or element 61 by demonstration of separation from praseodymium with potassium hydroxide fusions.

Positive identification of the 3.7y and the 11d radioisotopes was then achieved by the recently developed ion-exchange method using a synthetic organic cation exchanger (Amberlite IR-1) of the sulfonated phenolformaldehyde type. This new method provides very effective separations of the rare earths, even between adjacent elements. The procedure involves the absorption of the rare earth ions on a column of the resin from dilute acid solution followed by elution with 5% citric acid adjusted to a pH of about 3 with concentrated ammonia.

The order of elution of the rare earths (from lanthanum through europium and yttrium) was established in a series of experiments using radioactive cerium, lanthanum, europium and yttrium produced in fission and radioactive praseodymium and europium produced by slow neutron activation of pure oxides. Macroscopic quantities of samarium, europium, and neodymium with spectrographic analyses were also used. The results of these experiments show clearly that the order of elution of the rare earths is the reverse of that of atomic number, and that consequently the atomic number of an unknown radioisotope can be determined from the elution curves of a group of successive rare earths. Yttrium is eluted in the region of gadolinium as might be expected from its well known behavior in precipitation work. . . .

Considerable quantities of 61^{147} can be prepared as the result of the industrial application of nuclear power. A uranium pile operating at the power level of 1,000 kw. produces about 3×10^{16} fissions per second. . . . There is produced therefore, about 16 mg. per day of Nd^{147}, which, after suitable decay, is transformed into 61^{147} of sufficient half-life for isolation and chemical study.

Ion-Exchange Separation Method

➤ IN RECENT years, separation of the rare earths has been accomplished by a new technique that was developed for removing unwanted ions from solution. Originally used for water softening, the process makes use of the fact that salts, when they dissolve in water, split up into positive and negative ions. Certain materials have the ability to detain some of these ions as the water flows by.

Zeolites, which are naturally occurring compounds of silicon, were the first materials used for water softening in this manner. They would hold back the calcium ions, which make the water "hard," and substitute, from their own structure, unobjectionable sodium ions.

The process is more physical than chemical. The structure of the zeolite seems to resemble a minute honeycomb, in which the unwanted ions become entrapped. After long use these cells, known as reactive centers, become clogged with the borrowed ions, and must be regenerated by rinsing out with acids or a salt solution.

About 1935, chemists learned to make artificial ion-exchange resins which would behave like the zeolites. They soon improved upon nature, and developed a variety of these resins which would take out different kinds of ions, both positive and negative.

By a modification of the renegeration process, ions removed from one solution can be recovered with another. Thus mixtures of salts can be separated by removing one at a time. The mere trickling of a mixed solution down through ion-exchange resin packed in a long column will effect a surprising amount of separation, because each ion travels through the solution at its own speed. Other techniques that help the separation along can be added, such as varying the pH of the solution and washing out the ions to be salvaged with different "eluting" solutions.

Use of these techniques has solved the problem of separating the rare earths, which had plagued chemists ever since they were first discovered. Not only are the compounds of each one very much like those of all the rest, and of their analogues, but the elements have a strong tendency toward forming mixed compounds. The solubilities of the salts are affected by the various ions present in the solution.

For many years the only way to separate out one of the elements in even approximate purity was to make a long series of fractional crystallizations. Many salts of these elements are well known because chemists have hoped to find some that would differ in solubility enough to make the separation easier.

Salts that have been used most successfully for the purpose

include the sulfates, bromates, phosphates, nitrates, magnesium double nitrates, dimethyl phosphates, double sulfates with sodium, double carbonates with potassium, and others.

After preparing a saturated solution, the operator sets it aside until the first crystals form. These he tests, usually with a spectroscope, to determine their relative richness in the elements being separated. He then moves the crystals to a dish one place nearer the head of the line where that element is being concentrated. The solution from which they formed is moved in the opposite direction.

These "fractions" are recrystallized as the next step, and the process is repeated, often hundreds of times. The dishes holding the solutions are arranged fan-wise, the ones at the one side of the array holding the least soluble salts, the solubilities increasing toward the opposite side, as the operator patiently collects and combines the leftover solutions.

About one-quarter of the rare earth chemicals produced are used in carbon arc lighting applications. Rare-earth-cored carbons are indispensable to the motion picture industry, both in studio lighting and in theater projection. Searchlights also use rare-earth-cored carbons. Another quarter of the production is used in the form of mixed rare earth metal and cerium metal. Important also is the use in the glass industry. Cerium combined with iron makes the "flints" used in cigarette lighters. Protective goggles contain "didymium." With the earths more easily obtainable, more uses will undoubtedly be found for them.

The separation of the rare earths has become more than a laboratory exercise since atomic energy piles have gone into operation. Radioactive isotopes of yttrium, cerium, neodymium and other elements of the class appear in considerable quantities among the fission products of uranium.

Gallium

Gallium Predicted

THE NATURAL SYSTEM OF ELEMENTS *and its use for the Prediction of Properties of the Undiscovered Elements. By D. Mendeleeff in Journal of the Russian Chemical Society, Vol. 3, St. Petersburg, 1871. Translated by Taisia Stadnichenko.*

➤IN THIS GROUP [III] the element in the third series following zinc is lacking. Its atomic weight must be close to 68. We will call this element Ekaluminium, El=68, because it follows directly after aluminum in the third group [Ekaluminium= Gallium]. In distinction from Eb [Ekaboron=Scandium], it must possess the ability to form metallo-organic compounds, and because of its position between aluminium and indium it must have properties close to those two elements. Consequently it will form alums. Its hydroxide will be soluble in a water solution of potassium hydroxide. Its salts will be more stable than the salts of aluminium, thus Ekaluminium chloride will be more stable than aluminium chloride.

Its atomic volume, based on consideration of the same characters as were applied in determination of the properties of Ekaboron, must be close to 11.5, hence the specific weight in the metallic state will be near 6.0. The properties of this metal in all respects must represent the transition from the properties of aluminium to the properties of indium. It is very likely that the metal will possess greater volatility than aluminum, and therefore we may hope that it will be discovered by spectroinvestigation in the way indium and thallium following it have been discovered, although it will be less volatile than either of them and therefore we must not expect such striking spectral phenomena as led to the discovery of the latter. Most probably this element also does not belong to the number of cerium's satellites, although its equivalent approaches the equivalent of Yttrium. But it has not the form of oxide typical of Yttrium with the molecular formula RO, nor do the distinct basic properties of its oxide permit us to consider Yttrium as belonging to this place in the system of elements; instead the next place, in the third series, position III-4, belongs to Yttrium.

Gallium Discovered

SUR UN NOUVEAU MÉTAL, le Gallium, (On a new metal, Gallium) par M. Lecoq de Boisbaudran. Annales de Chimie et de Physique (5), Vol. X, 1877.

→ GALLIUM has been discovered too recently for its study to be well advanced. By reason of the excessive rarity of the new element in the first material examined up to now, the time elapsed since the determination of its existence has been principally given up first to research upon a practical method of its extraction, then to the treatment, always long in a small laboratory, of many hundred kilograms of the mineral; finally to the even more complicated purification so that the manner of gallium's behavior with many reagents is still unknown.

I can only give here a very incomplete account of gallium. This glimpse may nevertheless be sufficient, I hope, to serve as a basis for researches which other chemists may wish to undertake. . . .

On the 27th of August 1875, between 3 and 4 o'clock in the afternoon, I found the first indications of the existence of a new element, which I have named "gallium" in honor of France (Gallia).

Properties of Pure Gallium

Gallium is a gray-white metal, having a beautiful luster, but becoming tarnished quickly in humid air on account of superficial oxidation.

The color and the sheen are notably modified at the moment when the metal solidifies. In the liquid state (in superfusion, for example) it is a very beautiful silver white; but, if a point on its surface is touched with a bit of solid gallium, one sees a spot form which extends itself rapidly: it is the metal which, in crystallizing, takes on a very pronounced bluish color; at the same time the brilliance diminishes.

Gallium melts at the heat of the hand. . . .

Once solidified, gallium is hard and resistant, even to a few degrees above its point of fusion; it can, nevertheless, be cut, is flexible and malleable.

Above 30.15°, or in the cold when supercooled, gallium wets the glass and spreads over it, easily forming a beautiful mirror which seems to me to be whiter than that produced by mercury. On contact with tepid water gallium can easily be detached from the glass by rubbing.

The surface of the metal upon fusion is soon covered with a thin skin of metallic appearance, but doubtless formed of the oxide, under which is seen a little mobile stream when the flask is tilted.

Heated to bright red in the presence of air, gallium does not volatilize and is oxidized only very superficially. After cooling, it is sufficient to rub the metal with a rod to restore its luster.

If platinum foil covered with gallium is heated to redness, the latter element penetrates a little into the foil and begins to alloy with it, for hydrochloric acid no longer attacks it; it is nevertheless dissolved by aqua regia so weak that it will dissolve only traces of platinum. At the same time, a thin white skin is detached, formed probably of the oxide of gallium which calcination has rendered difficultly soluble in acids. The solution in aqua regia gives the spectrum of gallium.

Indium

PRELIMINARY NOTICE OF A NEW METAL. *By F. Reich and Th. Richter, Chemical News, Vol. 7-8, 1863.*

→THE AUTHORS have found a new metal in two Freiburg ores, which were composed principally of arsenical pyrites, blende, and some lead-glance, together with silica, manganese, copper, and a small proportion of tin and cadmium. The ores were first roasted to get rid of the greater part of the arsenic and sulfur, then mixed with hydrochloric acid, and distilled to dryness. The impure chloride of zinc obtained was examined with the spectroscope for thallium. No green line was seen, but the authors remarked an indigo-blue line, which was till then unknown.

The authors succeeded in isolating the conjectural substance, necessarily in very minute quantity, partly in the form of chloride, partly in the metallic state. On submitting these, moistened with hydrochloric acid, to the spectroscope, the blue line was seen so brilliant, sharp and persistent, that they did not hesitate to conclude that it belonged to a hitherto unrecognized metal, to which they accordingly gave the name *Indium*.

The line mentioned has a perceptibly greater refrangibility than the blue line of strontium, and there appears besides a much weaker line, of still greater refrangibility, which almost, but not quite, reaches the blue line of calcium.

The authors add that as far as they have examined the chemical properties of Indium they may safely assert that it is not precipitated from an acid solution of the chloride by sulphuretted hydrogen; that from the same solution it is precipitated by ammonia as a hydrated oxide; that the chloride is extremely deliquescent; and that the oxide heated on charcoal with soda gives lead-grey metallic beads, which are ductile and very soft; these heated again before the blowpipe give a yellowish slag, which, on further heating, takes no characteristic color with cobalt solution.

Thallium

ON THE EXISTENCE OF A NEW ELEMENT, *probably of the Sulfur Group. By William Crookes, Chemical News, Vol. 3, 1861.*

→In the year 1850 Professor Hoffman placed at my disposal upwards of ten pounds of the seleniferous deposit from the sulfuric acid manufactory at Tilkerode, in the Hartz Mountains, for the purpose of extracting from it the selenium, which was afterwards employed in an investigation upon the selenocyanides. Some residues which were left in the purification of the crude selenium, and which, from their reactions, appeared to contain tellurium, were collected together and placed aside for examination at a more convenient opportunity.

They remained unnoticed until the beginning of the present year, when, requiring some tellurium for experimental purposes, I attempted its extraction from these residues. Knowing that the spectra of the incandescent vapors of both selenium and tellurium were free from any strongly marked lines which might lead to the identification of either of these elements, it was not until I had in vain tried numerous chemical methods for isolating the tellurium which I supposed to be present, that the method of spectrum analysis was used.

A portion of the residue introduced into gas-flame gave abundant evidence of selenium; but as the alternate light and dark bands due to this element became fainter, and I was expecting the appearance of the somewhat similar but closer bands of tellurium, suddenly a *bright green line* flashed into view and quickly disappeared.

An isolated green line in this portion of the spectrum was new to me. I had become intimately acquainted with the appearance of most of the artificial spectra during many years' investigation, and had never before met with a similar line to this; and as, from the chemical processes through which this residue had passed, the elements which could possibly be present were limited to a few, it became of interest to discover which of them occasioned this green line.

After numerous experiments, I have been led to the conclusion, that it is caused by the presence of a new element. . . .

The properties of the substance both in solution and in the dry state, as nearly as I can make out from the small quantity at my disposal, are the following:—

1. It is completely volatile below a red heat both in the elementary state and in combination (except when united with a heavy fixed metal).

2. From its hydrochloric solution, it is readily precipitated by metallic zinc in the form of a heavy black powder, insoluble in the acid liquid.

3. Ammonia added very gradually until in slight excess to its acid solution gives no precipitate or coloration whatever, neither does the addition of carbonate or oxalate of ammonia to this alkaline solution.

4. Dry chlorine passed over it at a dull red heat unites with it, forming a readily volatile chloride soluble in water.

5. Sulphuretted hydrogen passed through its hydrochloric solution precipitates it incompletely, unless only a trace of free acid is present; but in an alkaline solution an immediate precipitation of a heavy black powder takes place.

6. Fused with nitre and carbonate of soda it becomes soluble in water, hydrochloric acid added in excess to this liquid producing a solution which answers to the above tests 2, 3 and 5.

An examination of these reactions shows that there are very few elements which could by the remotest possibility be mistaken for it.

Transactinium Earths

Actinide Series

ELEMENT	ELECTRON SHELLS
$_{90}$Th	$= K_2L_8M_{18}N_{32}O_{18}P_{10}Q_2$
$_{91}$Pa	$= K_2L_8M_{18}N_{32}O_{20}P_9Q_2$
$_{92}$U	$= K_2L_8M_{18}N_{32}O_{21}P_9Q_2$
$_{93}$Np	$= K_2L_8M_{18}N_{32}O_{22}P_9Q_2$
$_{94}$Pu	$= K_2L_8M_{18}N_{32}O_{24}P_8Q_2$
$_{95}$Am	$= K_2L_8M_{18}N_{32}O_{23}P_8Q_2$
$_{96}$Cm	$= K_2L_8M_{18}N_{32}O_{25}P_9Q_2$
$_{97}$Bk	$= K_2L_8M_{18}N_{32}O_{27}P_8Q_2$
$_{98}$Cf	$= K_2L_8M_{18}N_{32}O_{28}P_8Q_2$
$_{99}$Es	$= K_2L_8M_{18}N_{32}O_{29}P_8Q_2$
$_{100}$Fm	$= K_2L_8M_{18}N_{32}O_{30}P_8Q_2$
$_{101}$Md	$= K_2L_8M_{18}N_{32}O_{31}P_8Q_2$
$_{102}$No	$= K_2L_8M_{18}N_{32}O_{32}P_8Q_2$

➤Looking back upon the literature of the elements now known as the actinide series, one is struck by the many references to the similarity of thorium and the rare earths, especially cerium. Yet chemists kept trying to fit the elements heavier than radium into an imaginary periodic table constructed without reference to the series of elements now known as the lanthanides.

Niels Bohr, almost alone, recognized the relationship between atomic structure and the appearance of these fourteen extra elements, and warned chemists to expect a second rare earth series. But even he did not foretell the exact correspondence, element for element, that has become more apparent with each new transuranian element created by the Berkeley cyclotron.

While the oxide of thorium is not too unlike those of titanium and zirconium, the idea that element 91 would be like tantalum was a stumbling block in the way of finding it. Trying to force uranium into the pattern of chromium, molybdenum and tungsten was responsible for errors that delayed the atomic energy program.

The elements of the actinide series (thorium through the undiscovered element 103) show a strong chemical resemblance to the rare-earth or lanthanide group of elements. The resemblance between the lanthanide and actinide elements suggests that their electronic structure must also be similar. Evidence in the form of chemical properties, absorption and fluorescence spectra in aqueous solution and crystals, crystallographic-structure data, magnetic susceptibility data, and spectroscopic data indicates that an inner electron shell consisting of fourteen 5f electrons in the case of the actinide elements and fourteen 4f electrons in the case of the lanthanide elements is filled in progressing across the series.

Thorium is of importance in our nuclear power program in that it can be used to produce U^{233}, a long-lived fissionable isotope similar to U^{235}. In a so-called breeding reactor the following reaction can be made to occur:

$$Th^{232} \xrightarrow{n,\gamma} Th^{233} \xrightarrow{\beta^-} Pa^{233} \xrightarrow{\beta^-} U^{233}.$$

In principle, this and a similar reaction with U^{238} to yield Pu^{239} can be used to enlarge our supply of nuclear fuel from only U^{235} to the total available uranium and thorium.

Thorium

Thorium is widely distributed in the minerals of the earth's crust, the average thorium content being about 12 parts per million. Thorium metal is comparable to lead in density and to titanium in melting point, the melting point of thorium being close to 1750° C. In comparison to the structural metals, thorium has low strength. The metal is highly electropositive in character, being about as reactive as magnesium. Thorium usually shows only one oxidation state, the +4 state.

EXCERPT FROM UNTERSUCHUNG EINES NEUES MINERALS UND DARIN ENTHALTENEN ZUVOR UNBEKANNTEN ERDE (*Examination of a new mineral and a hitherto unknown earth contained in it*). *By J. J. Berzelius, in Annalen der Physik und Chemie, 1829.*

→THE MINERAL, the examination of which I am reporting here, occurs on Löv-ön, an island lying in the sea near Brevig in Norway, in syenite. It was itself discovered by Rev. Esmark, a son of the famous professor of mineralogy in the University of Christiana, Jens Esmark, who recently sent me a sample of this mineral for analysis, because, on account of its great specific gravity, he suspected tantalum in it. . . .

This mineral contains a hitherto unknown metallic body, which from its properties belongs to those which comprise the so-called true earths; its oxide is an earth, which is most like the earth of zircon, and which, strangely enough, possesses most of the properties and earmarks which I found for thorium earth in my former description of it. This circumstance at first made me think that thorium earth might possibly not be merely basic yttrium phosphate, as my later researches seem to prove, but a mixture of this and thorium earth. By this I was moved in the beginning to let the new earth have the name *Thorium earth.* . . . This offers at the same time an opportunity for naming the new mineral; I name it *Thorite.*

Protactinium*

THE ANALYTICAL CHEMISTRY OF ELEMENT 91, *Ekatantalum, and its Difference from Tantalum. By Aristid v. Grosse, Journal of the American Chemical Society, 52, 1930.*

➤IN 1871 Mendeleeff, on the basis of his periodic law, predicted the existence of a metal between thorium and uranium and named it ekatantalum (symbol Et). At present three isotopes of ekatantalum are known, all of them radioactive: brevium (Bv), discovered by Fajans in 1913, protoactinium (Pa) and uranium Z (UZ, O. Hahn).

Henceforth the author proposes to use as a synonym for element 91 the term "ekatantalum" (Et), meaning by it *all* the isotopes of element 91. . . .

Until recently all attempts to concentrate and isolate the new element have been unsuccessful. These attempts have been based on the assumption that an analogy exists between the properties of ekatantalum and tantalum similar to that between radium and barium. This assumption has been supported by the authority of many prominent chemists and was one of the principal reasons for failure in attempts to isolate ekatantalum.

In November 1926 the writer presented to Prof. O. Hahn a report entitled "The Properties of Protoactinium and its Compounds, Calculated According to the Periodic Law." The principal deductions were as follows:

Element 91, ekatantalum, will have its own characteristic properties and analytical reactions, differing from those of tantalum and columbium, just as its neighbors, thorium and uranium, differ greatly in their properties from their lower homologs, hafnium and zirconium, and tungsten and molybdenum.

Ekatantalum pentoxide (Et_2O_5) will have basic properties (similar to UO_3 and ThO_2) and form salts with acids, as contrasted with tantalum pentoxide (Ta_2O_5), which is a weak acid anhydride.

These predictions were verified recently through the isolation by the writer of 2 mg of element 91 in pure form as its oxide. Ekatantalum pentoxide, like tantalum pentoxide, is a heavy white powder with a very high melting point. The ignited oxide is practically insoluble in concentrated sulfuric, nitric or hydrochloric acid. . . .

* This is the newly adopted spelling for the element formerly called "protoactinium."

[Dr. v. Grosse then extracted 40 mg of element 91, and examined its behavior in parallel reactions with comparable quantities of tantalum compounds.]

A consideration of the reactions . . . shows that except for the precipitation by ammonia, a reaction characteristic of almost all metals, *ekatantalum* and *tantalum* have *only one reaction in common,* the insolubility of their oxides in hydrofluoric acid. . . .

The behavior of the pentoxides of the two metals toward various re-agents shows that while tantalum pentoxide is a feeble acid anhydride and forms more stable compounds with alkalies, ekatantalum pentoxide is a weak but decidedly basic oxide with no acidic properties.

Uranium

CHEMISCHE UNTERSUCHUNG DES URANITS, *einer neuentdeckten metallischen Substanz (Chemical Investigation of Uranium, a newly discovered metallic substance). By Prof. Klaproth, in Chemische Annalen für die Freunde der Naturlehre Arzneygelahrtheit, Haushaltungskunft und Manufacturen; von Lorenz Crell, IX, 1789.*

→ AMONG THE number of minerals of still unknown constitution, which hitherto, on this account, neither had nor could have a precise name nor a suitable place in the system, belongs the so-called Pitchblends from the mine of George Wahsfort at Johanngeorgenstadt. Misled by the name given to this ore by the common miner, it was formerly listed among the zinc ores, until Mr. Insp. Werner in Freyberg, to whom its cleavage, hardness and unusual weight gave sufficient proof that it could be no blende, put it with the iron earths, and named it *Eisenpecherz (ferrum ochraceum picem).*

[*In his "Mineral Substances" Klaproth details some of the experiments he tried with the new material.*]

All alkalis throw down the metallic portion from the acid solutions of pitchblende, of a yellow color. This affords another character peculiar to that metallic substance. The shades, or degradations of that yellow color, are various, according to the degrees of purity of the fossil, and, likewise, according to the nature of the alkaline salt employed in the process. . . .

If more carbonated alkali be added than is required to saturate the acid, part of the metallic oxide will be redissolved; but it falls down again, of a lemon-yellow, by neutralizing the excessive portion of the alkali. A similar redissolution, in carbonated fixed alkali, happens, when the yellow oxide, recently precipitated and washed, while yet moist, is mixed with deliquesced potash, and digested in boiling heat. If, to the saffron-yellow solution, after separation of the undissolved residue, nitric acid is added, it throws down the dissolved part of a pale yellow color.

On repeating this experiment with caustic lixivium, the color of the metallic oxide changed to a dark brown.

Somewhat different was the color of the precipitate which I have obtained from the greenish nitric solution of the blacker variety of pitchblende, by means of caustic soda; for this inclined from the yellow to the green. This is not owing to a latent portion of copper in the fossil; as the precipitate gives neither color nor taste to caustic ammoniac poured upon it.

The yellow metallic oxide, gently ignited, mixed with a proper flux, and applied to porcelain, and fused upon it in the enameling furnace, produced a saturated or deep orange-yellow color.

From these experiments it easily follows that this mineral substance belongs neither to the zinc ores nor to the iron ores, nor to the tungsten- or wolfram-containing minerals, moreover to none of the hitherto known mineral substances, but that it is a unique, independent, half-metallic substance in the system [of minerals]. It must consequently drop its present false names, as Pitchblende, Eisenpecherz, and must be given, on this account, a new, exclusive, specific name. Until the possible discovery of one still more fitting, I give it the name *Uranite*; which name I, after the example of the old philosophers, take from a planet, namely from the newest discovered, Uranus.

For more than a century, uranium remained just another element, until Henri Becquerel's discovery that it gives off rays which affect a photographic plate. This proved the cue for the discovery of the radioactive elements polonium, radium and actinium. Radioactivity as a new property of matter led to discovery of principles of atomic structure, and this, in turn, to finding uranium's fissionable isotope, U235. Fission makes atomic power available.

Excerpt from the following:

Sur les radiations emises par phosphorescence. (*About the radiations emitted by phosphorescence.*) *Note de M. Henri Becquerel. Comptes rendus, Vol. 122, page 420 (1896).*

At a previous meeting, M. Ch. Henry announced that phosphorescent zinc sulfide interposed in the path of rays emanating from a Crookes tube increases the intensity of the radiations passing through aluminum.

On the other hand, M. Niewenglowski has recognized that commercial phosphorescent calcium sulfide gives off radiations that pass through opaque substances.

That fact extends to different phosphorescent substances

and, in particular, to the salts of uranium in which the phosphorescence has a very short duration.

With potassium uranyl sulfate, of which I possess crystals
forming a thin and transparent crust, I was able to make the
following experiment:

A Lumière gelatine bromide photographic plate is wrapped
with two pieces of very thick black paper, such that the plate
is not clouded by exposure to the sun for a day.

On the outside of the piece of paper, there is placed a patch
of phosphorescent material, and the whole is exposed to the
sun for several hours. Following this when the photographic
plate is developed, it is found that the shape of the phosphorescent material appears in black on the negative. If there is
placed between the phosphorescent material and the paper a
coin or a metal screen pierced with a design, it is seen that an
image of these objects appears on the negative.

The same experiments can be repeated with there being
placed between the phosphorescent substance and the paper
a thin sheet of glass to exclude the possibility of a chemical
action due to the gases which could be given off from the
material warmed by the sun's rays.

It is possible to conclude from these experiments that the
phosphorescent substance in question emits radiations that
penetrate the paper opaque to light and reduce the silver salts.

Atomic Power

ATOMIC ENERGY FOR MILITARY PURPOSES. *By Henry D. Smyth, U. S. Government Printing Office, 1945.*

➤ OUR COMMON sources of power, other than sunlight and water power, are chemical reactions—usually the combustion of coal or oil. They release energy as the result of rearrangements of the outer electronic structures of the atoms, the same kind of process that supplies energy to our bodies. Combustion is always self-propagating; thus lighting a fire with a match releases enough heat to ignite the neighboring fuel, which releases more heat which ignites more fuel, and so on. In the nuclear reactions we have described this is not generally true; neither the energy released nor the new particles formed are sufficient to maintain the reaction. But we can imagine nuclear reactions emitting particles of the same sort that initiate them and in sufficient numbers to propagate the reaction in neighboring nuclei. Such a self-propagating reaction is called a "chain reaction" and such conditions must be achieved if the energy of the nuclear reactions with which we are concerned is to be put to large-scale use.

Although there were no atomic power plants built in the thirties, there were plenty of discoveries in nuclear physics and plenty of speculation. A theory was advanced by H. Bethe to explain the heat of the sun by a cycle of nuclear changes involving carbon, hydrogen, nitrogen, and oxygen, and leading eventually to the formation of helium.[1] This theory is now

[1] The series of reactions postulated was

$$(1) \quad _6C^{12} + {}_1H^1 \rightarrow {}_7N^{13}$$
$$(2) \quad _7N^{13} \rightarrow {}_6C^{13} + {}_1e^0$$
$$(3) \quad _6C^{13} + {}_1H^1 \rightarrow {}_7N^{14}$$
$$(4) \quad _7N^{14} + {}_1H^1 \rightarrow {}_8O^{15}$$
$$(5) \quad _8O^{15} \rightarrow {}_7N^{15} + {}_1e^0$$
$$(6) \quad _7N^{15} + {}_1H^1 \rightarrow {}_6C^{12} + {}_2He^4$$

The net effect is the transformation of hydrogen into helium and positrons (designated as $_1e^0$) and the release of about thirty million electron volts energy.

generally accepted. The discovery of a few (n, 2n) nuclear reactions (i.e., neutron-produced and neutron-producing reactions) suggested that a self-multiplying chain reaction might be initiated under the right conditions. There was much talk of atomic power and some talk of atomic bombs. . . .

Two general trends had been discovered in nuclear structure: first, that the proportion of neutrons goes up with atomic number; second, that the binding energy per particle is a maximum for the nuclei of intermediate atomic number. Suppose the U-238 nucleus is broken exactly in half; then, neglecting the mass of the incident neutron, we have two nuclei of atomic number 46 and mass number 119. But the heaviest stable isotope of palladium ($X = 46$) has a mass number of only 110. Therefore to reach stability each of these imaginary new nuclei must eject nine neutrons, becoming $_{46}Pd^{110}$ nuclei; or four neutrons in each nucleus must convert themselves to protons by emitting electrons, thereby forming stable tin nuclei of mass number 119 and atomic number 50; or a combination of such ejections and conversions must occur to give some other pair of stable nuclei. Actually, as was suggested by Hahn and Strassmann's identification of barium ($Z = 56$, $A = 135$ to 140) as a product of fission, the split occurs in such a way as to produce two unequal parts of mass numbers about 140 and 90 with the emission of a few neutrons and subsequent radioactive decay by electron emission until stable nuclei are formed. Calculations from binding-energy data show that any such rearrangement gives an aggregate resulting mass considerably less than the initial mass of the uranium nucleus, and thus that a great deal of energy must be released. . . .

Plutonium

It was realized that radiative capture of neutrons by U-238 would probably lead by two successive beta-ray emissions to the formation of a nucleus for which $Z = 94$ and $A = 239$. Consideration of the Bohr-Wheeler theory of fission and of certain empirical relations among the nuclei by L. A. Turner and others suggested that this nucleus would be a fairly stable alpha emitter and would probably undergo fission when bombarded by thermal neutrons. Later the importance of such thermal fission to the maintenance of the chain reaction was foreshadowed in private correspondence and discussion. In terms of our present knowledge and notation the particular reaction suggested is as follows:

$$_{92}U^{238} + _{0}n^{1} \rightarrow _{92}U^{239} \rightarrow _{93}Np^{239} + _{-1}e^{0}$$
$$_{93}Np^{239} \rightarrow _{94}Pu^{239} + _{-1}e^{0}$$

where Np and Pu are the chemical symbols now used for the two new elements, neptunium and plutonium; $_{0}n^{1}$ represents the neutron, and $-_1e^0$ represents an ordinary (negative) electron. Plutonium 239 is the nucleus rightly guessed to be fissionable by thermal neutrons. . . .

The principle of operation of an atomic bomb or power plant utilizing uranium fission is simple enough. If one neutron causes a fission that produces more than one new neutron, the number of fissions may increase tremendously with the release of enormous amounts of energy. It is a question of probabilities. Neutrons produced in the fission process may escape entirely from the uranium, may be captured by uranium in a process not resulting in fission, or may be captured by an impurity. Thus the question of whether a chain reaction does or does not go depends on the result of a competition among four processes: (1) escape; (2) non-fission capture by uranium; (3) non-fission capture by impurities; (4) fission capture.

If the loss of neutrons by the first three processes is less than the surplus produced by the fourth, the chain reaction occurs; otherwise it does not. Evidently any one of the first three processes may have such a high probability in a given arrangement that the extra neutrons created by fission will be insufficient to keep the reaction going. For example, should it turn out that process (2) —non-fission capture by uranium— has a much higher probability than fission capture, there would presumably be no possibility of achieving a chain reaction. . . .

Critical Size

The relative number of neutrons which escape from a quantity of uranium can be minimized by changing the size and shape. In a sphere any volume effect is proportional to the cube of the radius. Now the escape of neutrons from a quantity of uranium is a surface effect depending on the area of the surface, but fission capture occurs throughout the material and is therefore a volume effect. Consequently the greater the amount of uranium, the less probable it is that neutron escape will predominate over fission capture and prevent a chain reaction. Loss of neutrons by non-fission capture is a volume effect like neutron production by fission capture, so that increase in size makes no change in its relative importance.

The critical size of a device containing uranium is defined as the size for which the production of free neutrons by fission is just equal to their loss by ecape and by non-fission capture. . . .

Moderators

For some years before the discovery of fission, the customary way of slowing down neutrons was to cause them to pass through material of low atomic weight, such as hydrogenous material. It was E. Fermi and L. Szilard who proposed the use of graphite as a moderator for a chain reaction. . . .

It occurred to a number of physicists that it might be possible to mix uranium with a moderator in such a way that the high-speed fission neutrons, after being ejected from uranium and before re-encountering uranium nuclei, would have their speeds reduced below the speeds for which non-fission capture is highly probable. Evidently the characteristics of a good moderator are that it should be of low atomic weight and that it should have little or no tendency to absorb neutrons. Lithium and boron are excluded on the latter count. Helium is difficult to use because it is a gas and forms no compounds. The choice of moderator therefore lay between hydrogen, deuterium, beryllium, and carbon.

The Pile Operates

The pile was first operated as a self-sustaining system on December 2, 1942. So far as we know, this was the first time that human beings ever initiated a self-maintaining nuclear chain reaction. Initially the pile was operated at a power level of $\frac{1}{2}$ watt, but on December 12th the power level was raised to 200 watts.

Chemistry of Plutonium

The first isotope of plutonium discovered and studied was not the 239 isotope, which is an alpha-ray emitter with a half-life of about 50 years. U-238 bombarded with deuterons gives $_{93}Np^{238}$ which disintegrates to $_{94}Pu^{238}$ by beta emission.

Plutonium in the form of the isotope Pu^{238} was discovered by G. T. Seaborg, E. M. McMillan, J. W. Kennedy, and A. C. Wahl in late 1940 at the University of California at Berkeley. The element was produced by bombarding natural uranium with deuterons in the 60-inch cyclotron which led to the production of Np^{238} which decays with a 2-day half life to the isotope Pu^{238}. Later enough Pu^{238} was prepared to permit Seaborg, Kennedy and Wahl to begin the study of its chemical properties in the winter of 1940-41 by using tracer chemistry with carriers according to practice usual in radiochemistry. By such studies many chemical properties of plutonium were determined, and several possible chemical processes were evolved by which Pu-239 might be removed from the chain-reacting pile. The success of experiments on a tracer scale led to plans to produce enough Pu-239 to be treated as an ordinary substance on the ultra-microchemical scale. Such quantities were produced by prolonged bombardment of several hundred pounds of uranyl nitrate with neutrons obtained with the aid of cyclotrons, first at Berkeley and later at Washington University in St. Louis. By the end of 1942, something over 500 micrograms had been obtained in the form of pure plutonium salts. On August 18, 1942, B. B. Cunningham and L. B. Werner at the Metallurgical Laboratory isolated the first pure plutonium in the form of compounds of the isotope Pu^{239}; this was the first synthetic element to be isolated in pure form. Although this amount is less than would be needed to make the head of a pin, for the micro-chemists it was sufficient to yield considerable information; for one microgram is considered sufficient to carry out weighing experiments, titrations, solubility studies, etc.

From its position in the periodic table, plutonium might be expected to be similar to the rare earths or to uranium, thorium, or osmium. Which of these it will resemble most closely depends, of course, on the arrangement of the outermost groups of electrons and this arrangement could hardly have been predicted. On the whole, plutonium turned out to be more like uranium than like any of the other elements named. . . .

It was discovered fairly early that there were at least two states of oxidation of plutonium. It is now known to have the oxidation states of +3, +4, +5, and +6; the chemistry of plutonium is very complex owing to these multiple oxidation states and their relationship to each other.

Successful micro-chemical preparation of some plutonium salts and a study of their properties led to the general conclusion that it was possible to separate plutonium chemically from the other materials in the pile. This conclusion represents the attainment of the second immediate objective of the Metallurgical Laboratory. Chemical plants costing many millions of dollars were designed and built on the knowledge obtained from early experiments involving only microgram quantities of plutonium. Thus, by the end of 1942, plutonium, entirely unknown eighteen months earlier, was considered an element whose chemical behavior was as well understood as that of several of the elements of the old periodic table.

Neptunium

Element 93 was the first transuranium element to be discovered. The isotope Np^{239} was first produced by E. M. McMillan and P. H. Abelson in 1940 at the University of California at Berkeley by bombarding uranium with neutrons. Gram quantities of neptunium in the form of Np^{237} are currently being produced as a by-product from nuclear reactors. Neptunium has been found to have the oxidation states +3, +4, +5, and +6.

New Techniques and New Elements

→ WITH THE problem of uranium fission, chemists had to become familiar with the differences between individual isotopes of the elements. Soddy had coined the word *isotope* in 1913 to express the curious fact, learned by experience, that lead from radioactive ores is heavier than other lead.

This was a great shock to chemists, for atomic weight had always been considered an element's most stable property. When other elements obtained as the result of radioactive transformations were studied, they, too, were found to differ slightly in mass from samples of the same substance found in nature. Naturally occurring materials usually are found to consist of mixtures of several isotopes of their elements, occurring in constant proportions to one another.

The slight differences between the isotopes are reflected in such properties as solubilities, rates of diffusion, etc., when similar compounds of the pure isotopes of an element are compared. Such differences may be used to sort out one isotope from another.

Separation of isotopes was a problem of only mild academic interest until the discovery that 0.7% of natural uranium is the U-235 isotope, which is fissionable by slow neutrons, while the rest of the metal is the U-238 isotope, which prevents fission.

The story of how the separation of these isotopes was accomplished for the atomic bomb project has now become familiar. For the immediate purpose, an intensive study had to be made of uranium, a scarce and unfamiliar metal. This included a review of the literature which had been published about it since its discovery in 1789.

Much of the published information about uranium was found to be wrong, due to several factors. It was scarce and had found little use. Chemists supposed that it would be like chromium, molybdenum and tungsten, and misinterpreted some of their findings on that account. They were handicapped by lack of information about analogues of uranium, by which they could check their data.

Not only did knowledge of uranium need revision. Study of all the isotopes of all the elements had to be undertaken. Fission products coming from the atomic reactor proved to be made up of a great variety of elementary species.

Questions which immediately became acute were, on the theoretical side, how these atomic transformations take place, and, on the practical side, what can be done with these new radioactive materials being introduced into the world.

The general laws of atomic transformations are gradually

being worked out. When the 184-inch cyclotron at the University of California was put into operation in 1947, atoms were split on a more energetic scale than ever before, with the result that new isotopes of familiar elements, of lighter weight than any known previously appeared.

This process, christened *spallation,* of knocking heavy elements to pieces, produced much new information of extreme theoretical interest. It proved that, in general, alpha radiation (emission of helium nuclei) takes place from light, neutron-deficient atoms, while beta radiation (emission of electrons) comes from atoms too heavy for stability.

Various ways have been devised to measure the energies involved in these transformations. Probabilities of various kinds of nuclear reactions have been measured. Kinds of products can be predicted. Advantage can be taken of known laws to produce new nuclear species.

Elements are recognized among the products of nuclear reactions by the usual procedures of analytic chemistry, and radioactive isotopes are identified by their rates of radioactive "decay" into other substances. The chemist in this field, however, works with extremely small quantities of the material he hopes to identify. Special apparatus and techniques have been developed for handling test procedures on an ultra-microchemical scale.

When the analytical class to which the unknown radioactive material belongs has been determined, a known quantity of its closest chemical relative is often added to the solution. This acts as a carrier. Information about chemical characteristics, valence, states of oxidation, solubility, volatility and many other qualities can then be obtained by following the radiation with suitable counters as it stays with, or is separated from, the visible amounts of carrier material.

It was in this way that the preliminary specifications for building the plutonium plant at Hanford, Washington, were worked out, using quantities of the unidentified metal plutonium so small that they were invisible.

Design of the plant for operation by remote control was another complication in that fabulous project. This was necessary because the large quantities of material handled, both uranium and plutonium, besides being chemically poisonous, are so strongly radioactive that no one could survive working among the radiations they give off.

After irradiation for a predetermined length of time, the uranium with which this pile is charged is pushed out into a solvent in which the newly-formed plutonium ions are set free. While there is considerable chemical similarity between uranium and plutonium, each can act with several valences to form series of compounds. By taking advantage of these properties, it is possible to precipitate the plutonium fissionable isotope, Pu-239, and purify it for further processing.

Side reactions in the plutonium plant form neptunium. The isotope Np-237 is an alpha-emitter with low enough activity so that it can be accumulated and handled in milligram amounts with relative safety. This isotope made practical the determination of neptunium's chemical properties.

Transmutation of one element into another is as precise a reaction as is the formation of a chemical compound. Nuclear equations must balance, and reactions are specific for each isotope. Types of reactions are known which can be used to predict the probable outcome of untried transformations. It is necessary, however, in order to obtain a particular product, to start with the right isotope and to furnish the necessary energy.

Ion exchange is one of the most important experimental methods used in the study of the chemical properties of most of the actinide elements. This technique together with the element by element analogy between the corresponding actinide and lanthanide elements has been the key to the discovery of the transcurium elements.

Americium, Curium, Berkelium, Californium, Einsteinium, Fermium, Mendelevium and Nobelium

After the successful production of two man-made elements, it was natural to try the synthesis of further novel elements. Glenn T. Seaborg and his associates, working at the Metallurgical Laboratory of the University of Chicago during World War II, produced first No. 96, curium 242, and afterward No. 95, americium 241, from plutonium 239. The reactions by which they were produced are:

$$_{94}Pu^{239} + _{2}He^{4} \rightarrow _{96}Cm^{242} + _{0}n^{1}$$ and:

$$_{94}Pu^{239} + _{0}n^{1} \rightarrow _{94}Pu^{240}$$

$$_{94}Pu^{240} + _{0}n^{1} \rightarrow _{94}Pu^{241}$$

$$_{94}Pu^{241} (\beta^{-}/14\,yr) \rightarrow _{95}Am^{241}$$

Berkelium (element 97), the fifth transuranium element to be synthesized, was discovered by S. G. Thompson, A. Ghiorso, and G. T. Seaborg in late 1949 at the University of California in Berkeley. The isotope Bk^{243} was produced by the helium ion bombardment of Am^{241}.

Element 98, californium, in the form of the isotope Cf^{245} was produced by S. G. Thompson, K. Street, Jr., A. Ghiorso, and G. T. Seaborg at the University of California in Berkeley by the helium ion bombardment of microgram quantities of Cm^{242}. The element was first produced in early 1950.

Einsteinium and fermium, elements 99 and 100, were formed in the "Mike" thermonuclear explosion staged in the Pacific in 1952. The elements were discovered by scientists from the University of California Radiation Laboratory, Argonne National Laboratory, and Los Alamos Scientific Laboratory. Very heavy uranium isotopes formed by the action of the instantaneous neutron flux on the uranium in the device decayed into elements 99 and 100 and other transuranium elements.

Mendelevium, element 101, was first produced and identified by A. Ghiorso, B. G. Harvey, G. R. Choppin, S. G. Thompson, and G. T. Seaborg at the University of California in Berkeley in 1955 as the result of the bombardment of extremely small amounts of E^{253} with helium ions in the Berkeley 60-inch cyclotron. This was a notable accomplishment in that only one or two atoms of mendelevium per experiment were produced.

Americium, curium, berkelium, californium, and einsteinium can be produced by the intense neutron bombardment of Pu^{239} in, for example, the Materials Testing Reactor at Arco, Idaho. Americium is now produced in gram quantities. Curium, berkelium, and californium are available in weighable amounts, and this should soon be true for the einsteinium isotope with mass number 254 (half life 320 days). Since the longest lived fermium isotope known is Fm^{255} (half life 22 hours), it seems improbable that this element can ever be obtained in weighable amount. Mendelevium appears to have no long lived isotopes, and it seems improbable that this element will ever be isolated in weighable amount.

An isotope of element 102, probably 102^{251} or 102^{253}, was reported produced at the Nobel Institute for Physics in Stockholm, Sweden, in the spring of 1957 by a team of scientists from England, Sweden, and the United States. The synthesis was reportedly accomplished by bombarding Cm^{244} with $C^{13(+4)}$ ions and decayed by the emission of 8.5 Mev alpha particles with a half life of about 10 minutes. The name nobelium was suggested by this group for the element. Repeated experiments at the University of California Radiation Laboratory failed to confirm this discovery and in April, 1958, A. Ghiorso, T. Sikkeland, J. R. Walton and Glenn T. Seaborg identified the isotope 102^{254} as a product of the bombardment of Cm^{246} with C^{12} ions accelerated in the new heavy ion linear accelerator (HILAC) at Berkeley. The name of nobelium was not accepted by the Berkeley group. In the USSR, G. N. Flerov and his group in experiments starting in 1957 continued into 1958 produced an isotope, emitting 8.8 0.5 Mev alpha particles in the bombardment of Pu^{241} (and Pu^{242}) with high energy O^{16} ions accelerated in their cyclotron. It is quite possible that this alpha activity is due to the isotope 102^{254} identified by the California group.

The chemical properties of all the transuranium elements have been found to be very similar. All have electropositive trivalent ions which form inorganic complex ions and organic chelates. These elements form soluble sulfates, nitrates, chlorides, and perchlorates, and acid-insoluble trifluorides and oxalates. Neptunium, plutonium, and americium have higher oxidation states in aqueous solution; however, the stability of these states compared with the trivalent state decreases with increasing atomic number. In aqueous solution, berkelium has the oxidation states of three and four.

Future Elements. It is thought that elements 103 through about 108 will eventually be produced by bombarding uranium and the transuranium elements with heavy ions such as neon ions. The half lives of these elements will be so short that chemical identification will be difficult up to element 104 or 105 and almost impossible beyond these. Completion of the actinide group should occur with element 103 and the next five elements with atomic numbers 104 to 108 should be chemical homologues of the known elements with atomic numbers 72 (hafnium) to 76 (osmium).

The Carbon Group

Group IVb

ELEMENT   ELECTRON SHELLS

$_6C = K_2L_4$

$_{14}Si = K_2L_8M_4$

$_{32}Ge = K_2L_8M_{18}N_4$

$_{50}Sn = K_2L_8M_{18}N_{18}O_4$

$_{82}Pb = K_2L_8M_{18}N_{32}O_{18}P_4$

Carbon

→CARBON in its elemental state is most interesting because of its very different allotropic forms, graphite and diamond. The hardness, clarity and brilliance of a colorless diamond crystal contrasts dramatically with the soft, smudgy blackness of carbon as soot or as graphite such as is used in making "lead" pencils. Recent work on graphite for the structure of atomic energy piles has, however, revealed different qualities of the graphite so prepared. It is dark gray instead of black, does not rub off when handled, and has a hardness and texture approaching those of metal.

In its compounds, carbon is the unique element in so far as life is concerned. Its ability to join with other carbon atoms to build up compounds of great complexity accounts for the amazing variety characteristic of the forms of living matter.

The term "organic chemistry" is often used to describe the carbon compounds, which form a science in themselves. A mysterious life force was at one time thought essential to their formation. An important date in the history of chemistry was Wöhler's synthesis of urea in 1828. Then, for the first time, a compound known only as a product of life processes, was duplicated in the laboratory by using inorganic chemicals.

Wöhler was a friend of Liebig, who recognized the role of atmospheric carbon dioxide in the cycle of life. This was one of the early steps toward understanding photosynthesis, the method by which plants utilize the sun's energy.

Diamond, as the most brilliant jewel and the hardest abrasive, is one of the most glamourous materials known. Diamonds are found in volcanic rock, and have dropped to earth

113

in meteorites. The assumption has therefore been made that they crystallize from molten rock, and the French chemist, Henri Moissan, tried to make them artificially in his electric furnace. He claimed to have succeeded.

Modern investigation of the thermodynamics of carbon, however casts doubt on the possibility of Moissan's diamonds being formed by his method. Dr. Frederick D. Rossini has worked out the changes of state characteristic of carbon over wide ranges of temperature and pressure, and finds that diamond seems to be the more stable form of carbon when the temperature is very low, and graphite when heat and pressure are increased. Experiments by Dr. P. W. Bridgman at extreme pressures failed to produce the diamond form of carbon.

Carbon and Life

ORGANIC CHEMISTRY *in its applications to Agriculture and Physiology. By Justis Liebig. Edited from the manuscript of the author by Lyon Playfair. First American edition, with an introduction, notes and appendix, by John W. Webster, Cambridge, Mass., 1841. (First published 1837.)*

→ IT IS quite evident, that the quantities of carbonic acid and oxygen in the atmosphere, which remain unchanged by lapse of time, must stand in some fixed relation to one another; a cause must exist which prevents the increase of carbonic acid, by removing that which is constantly forming; and there must be some means of replacing the oxygen, which is removed from the air by the processes of combustion and putrefaction, as well as by the respiration of animals.

Both these causes are united in the process of vegetable life.

The facts which we have stated in the preceding pages prove, that the carbon of plants must be derived exclusively from the atmosphere. Now, carbon exists in the atmosphere only in the form of carbonic acid; and, therefore, in a state of combination with oxygen.

It has been already mentioned likewise, that carbon and the elements of water form the principal constituents of vegetables; the quantity of the substances which do not possess this composition being in very small proportion. Now, the relative quantity of oxygen in the whole mass is less than in carbonic acid. It is therefore certain that plants must possess the power of decomposing carbonic acid, since they appropriate its carbon for their own use. The formation of their principal component substances must necessarily be attended with the separation of the carbon of the carbonic acid from the oxygen, which must be returned to the atmosphere, whilst the carbon enters into combination with water or its elements. The atmosphere must thus receive a volume of oxygen for every volume of carbonic acid which has been decomposed. . . .

The presence of a rich and luxuriant vegetation may be conceived without the concurrence of animal life, but the existence of animals is undoubtedly dependent upon the life and development of plants.

Plants not only afford the means of nutrition for the growth and continuance of animal organization, but they likewise furnish that which is essential for the support of the important vital process of respiration; for besides separating all noxious matters from the atmosphere, they are an inexhaustible source of pure oxygen, which supplies the loss which the air is constantly sustaining. Animals, on the other hand, expire carbon, which plants inspire; and thus the composition of the medium in which both exist, namely, the atmosphere, is maintained constantly unchanged.

Silicon

As carbon is the most fundamental element in vegetation, its next heavier analogue, silicon, appears most frequently in quartz and feldspar which form typical rocks making up the outer crust of the earth. Both elements, indeed, are essential to the appearance of the earth as we know it, for other rocks are made up of carbonates, and silica contributes rigidity to the structure of plants.

Chemically silicon lacks carbon's ability to build up atom chains, but similar structures are formed when alternating atoms of silicon and oxygen join. The resulting compounds have recently come under chemical investigation, under the name of *silicones*. They can to some extent parallel the compounds of carbon, and also join with them to form new series of compounds with useful characteristics.

Silicon Discovery

Extract from ANNALS OF PHILOSOPHY, *new series, Vol. VII, London, 1824.*

→A LETTER from Professor Berzelius to the President [of the Royal Society] was read in which he describes the results of various chemical researches in which he has recently been engaged; and several memoirs on which accompanied the letter. . . .

The fifth memoir relates to the combinations of fluoric acid. A portion of this memoir now printing describes a method by which the author has succeeded in obtaining the base of silicon in an insulated state. It consists in acting by potassium on dry silicated fluate of potash, by which means a mixture of various substances is obtained, which yields hydroguret of silicon by being well washed with water; and when that substance is heated in a crucible the hydrogen is burned off, and the silicon obtained pure. Prof. B. then proceeds to give the results of various experiments upon this substance; among which are the following.

It is obtained in various states of aggregation, and its combustibility varies accordingly, it much resembling carbon in this respect: as usually obtained it is combustible when ignited in atmospheric air and in oxygen gas; but in its densest state it may become incandescent in the air without burning. It is very difficult to effect its complete combustion: 200 parts of silicon unite to 208 of oxygen to become silica. It will not burn when heated with nitre, but is brought into combustion by carbonate of potash; a curious circumstance which the author attributes to certain relations of affinities.

Silicon burns when ignited in chlorine, forming with it a transparent colorless fluid, having the smell of cyanogen. It is combustible in vapor of sulfur, producing a gray sulfuret, but cannot in this case be completely burned.

Prof. B. next describes the results of the same mode of decomposition as applied to ittria, glucina, and zirconia; giving the chemical habitudes of zirconium, which can be obtained in larger quantities than the bases of the former earths. He then states that he has used the term *fluate* instead of *fluoride* throughout this letter, not because he thinks the President's ingenious theory on the subject less probable than his own (though he has not been able, by his own experiments, to determine which is the true one); but because, as he was writing in a language foreign to him, he wished to employ the plainest terms: and concludes by requesting Sir Humphry to lay the above results before the Royal Society.

Germanium

Germanium has to a much slighter degree the power of forming organic-type compounds, and they have not as yet become of more than theoretical interest. Germanium is also of interest as the element which fulfills Mendeleeff's prediction of "Ekasilicon." But the metal itself has been found to have unique properties as a semi-conductor for use in radio and other electronic circuits. It is used for the *transistor*, the new substitute for the vacuum tube.

Ekasilicon

THE NATURAL SYSTEM OF ELEMENTS *and its use for the Prediction of Properties of the Undiscovered Elements. By D. Mendeleeff, in Journal of the Russian Chemical Society, Vol. 3, St. Petersburg, 1871. Translated by Taisia Stadnichenko.*

➤ IT SEEMS to me that the most interesting of the undoubtedly absent metals will be that which belongs to group IV of the analogues of carbon, namely to the third series. It will be the metal directly following silicon, and therefore we will call it Ekasilicon. Ekasilicon must have an atomic weight of about 72, because it is followed in this series by arsenic. In character, Ekasilicon will have properties intermediate between silicon and tin, just as Ekaluminum must have properties intermediate between aluminum and indium. . . .

Its properties will resemble the properties of Si and As to such an extent as the properties of As itself resemble the properties of P and Se, that is, it will at any rate be a fusible metal capable at high temperatures of voltalizing and oxidizing. It will decompose water vapor with difficulty. It will have almost no action on acids, that is, it will not liberate hydrogen and it will form very unstable salts. Alkalies will react on it similarly to their action on zinc and arsenic. . . .

Semi-Conductor

Extracts from CONDUCTIVITY IN SEMI-CONDUCTORS *by K. Lark-Horovitz in Electrical Engineering, Dec. 1949.*

→WHILE it is well known that the electrical conductivity of metals decreases with increasing temperature, there is a number of metallic-looking substances which show an entirely different behavior. These substances show low conductivity at low temperature, the conductivity increases as the temperature is raised, reaches a maximum, decreases again, and finally increases another time and much more sharply when a higher temperature is reached.

This behavior can be completely understood on the assumption that the number of current carriers in these substances is dependent on temperature. These materials are called, because of their behavior, semi-conductors.

At low temperatures, the number of carriers is small; ideally it should be zero at absolute zero and the semi-conductor would become an insulator. As the temperature increases, a greater number of carriers becomes available by dissociation from impurity centers and the conductivity increases. When all of the carriers from impurity centers have been released, their number remains constant until new carriers are released from another source at higher temperature. In the meantime with increasing temperature the probability of collision with the atoms present in the lattice of the semi-conductor becomes more frequent, the mean free path decreases, and as a consequence the resistance increases with temperature rise.

There is, however, the possibility that at higher temperatures more electrons might be freed from the semi-conductor itself and not from impurities. These so-called intrinsic electrons are available in far greater numbers than the total numbers of carriers which are freed from impurity centers (one per impurity center) and as a consequence the resistance at elevated temperatures decreases very rapidly. It is possible that one might find electron acceptors, instead of donators, in the semi-conductor.

These acceptor impurities have the peculiar quality, not of giving off electrons with rising temperature, but of taking up electrons. As a consequence, there remains a "hole" in the electron distribution. This "hole" has the properties of a "positive" electron and an effective mass which may differ from the mass of the free electron. Thus, it is possible to create a conductor of electricity which conducts by particles which behave as free electrons, except that their effective mass may differ from the mass of the electron and that their charge is of opposite sign. Such a conductor seems to conduct by positive charges.

Silicon and germanium are elements of the fourth group of the periodic table with the same crystal structure as the diamond and they have, respectively, 5.2×10^{22} and 4.5×10^{22} atoms per cubic centimeter. It has been found that the addition of impurity elements of the third group, such as boron, aluminum, gallium and indium, give defect or P-type (hole) conductivity. Additions of impurity elements from the fifth group, such as nitrogen, phosphorus, antimony, and arsenic, give excess or N-type (electron) conductivity. . . .

It is possible to determine the sign of the carriers in various ways. One method is to measure the transverse electromotive force produced in a material if a current flows through the material and a magnetic field is applied normal to the direction of current flow. (Hall effect).

A second simple way of determining the sign of carriers is the determination of the sign of the thermo-electric power, and finally, a third method is by observation of the direction of rectification, which usually can be predicted. . . .

The preparation of semiconductors with definite predictable properties based upon the addition of impurity atoms would be ideal if the new atoms could be placed at the lattice sites occupied by the original atoms, without disturbing the rest of the material. In principle this can be accomplished by exposing pure semi-conductors to slow (thermal) neutrons, which are absorbed with the emission of gamma rays and produce radioactive nuclei, which disintegrate, leaving stable new atoms in place of the original semi-conductor atoms and their isotopes. In the case of germanium the number and type of isotopes is quite well known, and it is also known that transmutation can lead to the formation of new atoms, namely gallium, which will produce P-type conduction, and arsenic, which will produce N-type conduction.

Tin and Lead

Tin and lead, the heaviest members of the carbon group, are among the seven original metals, identified with the planets Jupiter (bright) and Saturn (dull) respectively. In conformity with the usual trend, the elements of this group become markedly more metallic with increase in their atomic weights. Lead possesses unusual interest because it is the end-product of all the four chains of atomic disintegration by radioactivity.

Lead isotopes of atomic mass 206, 207 and 208 have been found in nature as stable disintegration products of U-238, U-235 and Th-232 respectively. By dividing each of these numbers by 4 it is easy to see the pattern of their structure, which holds through the series of disintegration products. Lead-206 results from U-238 disintegration. The formula for this series is $4n + 2$. U-235 decays to Pb-207. This formula is $4n + 3$. Th-232 decays to Pb-208. In this case the products follow the formula $4n$. The fourth series, $4n + 1$, was mysteriously lacking until disintegration products of Np proved to be members of a new series corresponding to that formula, which includes the missing elements At (85) and Fr (87). This takes in radioactive Pb-209 which changes to Bi-209 as the final stable product.

Early Methods of Assaying
Excerpt from the following:

GEORGIUS AGRICOLA DE RE METALLICA *translated from the first Latin edition of 1556, by Herbert Clark Hoover and Lou Henry Hoover. Published for the Translators by The Mining Magazine, Salisbury House, London, 1912.*

Lead
➤ LEAD ORE may be assayed by this method: crush half an *uncia* of pure lead-stone and the same quantity of the *chrysocolla* which they call borax, mix them together, place them in a crucible, and put a glowing coal in the middle of it. As soon as the borax crackles and the lead-stone melts, which soon occurs, remove the coal from the crucible, and the lead will settle to the bottom of it; weigh it out, and take account of that portion of it which the fire has consumed. If you also wish to know what portion of silver is contained in the lead, melt the lead in the cupel until all of it exhales. . . .

Tin
You can assay tin ore by the following method. First roast it, then crush, and afterward wash it; the concentrates are again roasted, crushed, and washed. Mix one and a half *cen-*

tumpondia of this with one *centumpondium* of the *chrysocolla*
which they call borax; from the mixture, when it has been
moistened with water, make a lump. Afterwards, perforate a
large round piece of charcoal, making this opening a palm
deep, three digits wide on the upper side and narrower on the
lower side. . . . Let it be placed in a crucible, and let glowing
coal be put round it on all sides; when the perforated piece of
coal begins to burn, the lump is placed in the upper part of the
opening, and it is covered with a wide piece of glowing coal,
and after many pieces of coal have been put round it, a hot
fire is blown up with the bellows, until all the tin has run
out . . . into the crucible.

The Nitrogen Group

Group Vb

ELEMENT	ELECTRON SHELLS
$_7N$	$= K_2L_5$
$_{15}P$	$= K_2L_8M_5$
$_{33}As$	$= K_2L_8M_{18}N_5$
$_{51}Sb$	$= K_2L_8M_{18}N_{18}O_5$
$_{83}Bi$	$= K_2L_8M_{18}N_{32}O_{18}P_5$

➔ CHEMICALS of life and death occupy this group. Nitrogen not only dilutes the air, as 18th century chemists learned, but builds the protein on which we live. Built into the endothermic chemicals like TNT, for which nitrogen is famous, its compounds can absorb energy when they are formed and turn it loose with catastrophic results when they explode.

Phosphorus not only shines in the dark, but plays a more important role in life processes than was realized until recently. Photosynthesis is now found to depend, for its first steps, on compounds of phosphorus with carbonate material.

Arsenic is the villain among chemicals for the poisonous quality of its compounds, yet it finds use for some industrial purposes. Antimony and bismuth find some uses in medicine.

Nitrogen

Extracts from EXPERIMENTS AND OBSERVATIONS *on Different Kinds of Air. By Joseph Priestley, Birmingham, 1790.*
➔ READING in Dr. Hale's account of his experiments, that there was a great diminution of the quantity of air in which had been exposed a mixture of powdered sulfur and filings of iron, made into a paste with water, I repeated the experiment, and found the diminution greater than I had expected. This diminution of air is made as effectually, and as expeditiously, in quicksilver as in water; and it may be measured with the greatest accuracy, because there is neither any previous expansion, or increase, of the quantity of air, and because it is some time before this process begins to have any sensible ef-

fect. This diminution of air is various; but I have generally found it to be between one fifth and one fourth of the whole.

Air thus diminished is not heavier, but rather lighter than common air.

I conclude that the diminution of air by this process is of the same kind with the diminution of it in the other cases, because when this mixture is put into air which has been previously diminished, either by the burning of candles, by respiration, or putrefaction, though it never fails to diminish it something more, it is, however, no farther than this process alone would have done it. If a fresh mixture be introduced into a quantity of air which had been reduced by a former mixture, it has little or no farther effect. . . .

Air diminished by this mixture of iron filings and sulfur is exceedingly noxious to animals, and I have not perceived that it grows any better by keeping in water. The smell of it is at first very pungent and offensive, which must be owing to a quantity of vitriolic acid air generated in the proccess.

The quantity of this mixture which I made use of in the preceding experiments was from two to four ounce measures; but I did not perceive but that the diminution of the quantity of air (which was generally about twenty ounce measures) was as great with the smallest as with the largest quantity. How small a quantity is necessary to diminish a given quantity of air to a *maximum,* I have made no experiments to ascertain.

Phosphorus

Extracts from THE AERIAL NOCTILUCA: *or some New Phaenomena, and a Process of a factitious self-shining Substance. In the Works of the Hon. Robert Boyle, London, 1722. [This paper was originally written about 1677].*

→ AFTER the experienced chymist Mr. Daniel Kraft had, in a visit that he purposely made me, shewn me and some of my friends, both his liquid and consistent phosphorus, being by the phaenomena I then observed (and whereof the curious have since had publick notice), made certain, that there is really such a factitious body to be made, as would shine in the dark, without having been before illustrated by any lucid substance, and without being hot as to sense: after this, I say, I took into consideration, by what ways it might be most probable, to produce, by art, such a shining substance. To seek for which I was both inclined, and hopeful to be somewhat assisted, because I had lying by me, among my yet unpublished notes of the mechanical origin of divers qualities, a collection of some observations and thoughts concerning light.

And I was also the more encouraged to attempt somewhat this way, because having, at Mr. Kraft's desire, imparted to him somewhat, that I discovered about uncommon mercuries (which I had then communicated but to one person in the world) he, in requital, confest to me at parting, that at least the principal matter of his phosphoruses was somewhat that belonged to the body of man. This intimation, though but very general, was therefore very welcome to me, because, though I have often thought it probable, that a shining substance may, by spagyrical art, be obtained from more kinds of bodies than one: yet designing in the first place, to try, if I could hit upon such a phosphorus as I saw was preparable, the advertisement saved me (for some time) the labour of ranging among various bodies, and directed me to exercise my industry in a narrower compass.

But there being divers parts of the human body, that have been taken to task by chymists, and, perhaps, by me as carefully, as by some others, my choice might have been distracted between the blood, the solid excrements, the bones, the urine, and the hair, of the human body; if various former trials and speculations upon more than one of those subjects had not directed me to pitch upon that, which was fittest to be chosen, and of which, as I had formerly set down divers experiments and observations, so I had made provision of a quantity of it, and so far prepared it, that it wanted but little of being fit for my present purpose. . . .

Adhering to the first choice I had made of a fit matter, I did not desist to work upon it by the ways I judged most hopeful, when a learned and ingenious stranger, (*A.G.*, M.D., countryman, if I mistake not, to Mr. Kraft who had newly made an excursion into *England*, to see the country, having, in a visit he was pleased to make me, occasionally discoursed, among other things, about the German noctiluca, whereof he soon perceived I knew the true matter, and had wrought much upon it; he said something about the degree of fire, that made me afterwards think, when I reflected on it, that that was the only thing I wanted to succeed in my endeavors. . . .

In this narrative I have been the more particular, that it may shew you, (what I hope may make you amends for the length of it) that an inquisitive man should not always be deterred by the difficulties, or even disappointments he may meet with, in prosecuting a noble experiment, as long as he judges himself to proceed upon good and rational grounds.
. . .

There was taken a considerable quantity of human urine, (because the liquor yields but a small proportion of luceriferous matter), that had been, (a good part of it at least) for a competent while, digested and putrified, before it was used. This liquor was distilled with a moderate heat, till the spirituous parts were drawn off; after which, the superfluous moisture also was abstracted, (or evaporated away) till the remaining substance was brought to the consistence of a somewhat thick syrup, or a thin extract. This was well incorporated with about thrice its weight of fine sand, and the mixture was put into a strong retort; to which was joined a large receiver, in good part filled with water. Then, the two vessels being carefully luted together, a naked fire was gradually administered for five or six hours, that all, that was either phlegmatic, or otherwise volatile, might come over first.

When this was done, the fire was increased, and at length, for five or six hours made, (N.B. which it should be in this operation) as strong and intense, as the furnace (which was not bad) was capable of giving. By this means, there came over good store of white fumes, almost like those, that appear in the distillation of oil of vitriol; and when those fumes were past, and the receiver grew clear, they were after a while succeeded by another sort, that seemed in the receiver to give a faint bluish light, almost like that of little burning matches dipt in sulphur. And last of all, the fire being very vehement, there passed over another substance, that was judged more ponderous than the former, because (N.B.) much of it fell through the water to the bottom of the receiver: whence being taken out, (and partly even whilst it staid there) it appeared by several effects, and other phaenomena, to be (as we expected) of a luceriferous nature.

The ways I employed to make a self-shining substance, out of other matters than that expressed in this process, I must, for certain reasons, forbear to acquaint you with, at this time.

Arsenic

→ ARSENIC is one of the elements used by the alchemists, but information about its discovery is lost. The alchemist's recipe, quoted here as an example of early work with arsenic, shows the kind of experiments the ancients did. They worked in the dry way and by distillation. Changing the color of metals was in their minds the first step toward transmutation.

COLLECTION DES ANCIENS ALCHIMISTES GRECS (*Collection of Ancient Greek Alchemists*) *par M. Berthelot*[1], *avec la Collaboration de M. Ch.-Em. Ruelle. Paris, Georges Steinheil, 1887.)*

Olympiodorus, Philosopher of Alexandria.

[1] Berthelot is the authority on the earliest alchemists whose Greek texts are preserved in libraries of Europe. Olympiodorus was a Greek historian and alchemist who was born in Thebes, Egypt, in the latter part of the fourth century A.D. In 412 he was a member of an embassy sent by the Emperor Honorius to Attila, the Hun.

➤ FIRST TINCTURE, coloring copper white by means of arsenic, as follows.

Arsenic (sulphidc) is a kind of sulphur which volatilizes quickly; that is to say, volatilizes over the fire. All substances similar to arsenic are also called sulphurs and volatile bodies. Now the preparation is made thus: taking 14 ounces of lamellar arsenic the color of gold, cut it into pieces, grind it so as to reduce it to particles as fine as down; then soak it in vinegar for two or three days and as many nights, the material being closed up in a glass vessel with a narrow neck, carefully luted at the top so that it shall not be dissipated. Shaking once or twice a day, do this for several days; then, emptying the vessel, wash with pure water, only just until the odor of vinegar has disappeared. Guard the most subtle part of the substance; and do not let it be thrown out with the water. After allowing the mass to dry and contract in the air, mix and pulverize with 5 ounces of salt of Cappadocia.

Now the use of the salt was devised by the ancients to avoid the arsenic sticking to the glass vessel. This glass vessel is called *asympoton* by Africanus. It is luted with clay; a glass cover in the shape of a cup is placed above. At the upper part, another cover envelopes the whole; it is fastened tightly on all sides, so that the distilled arsenic may not be dissipated.

Then distill it repeatedly and pulverize it, until it becomes white; thus we obtain a white and compact alum.[2] Then melt the copper with some hard Nicean copper; then take some of the flower of soda and throw into the bottom of the crucible 2 or 3 parts to flux it. Next add the dry powder (sublimed arsenic), with an iron ladle; put in the amount of one ounce to 2 pounds of copper. After that, put into the crucible for each ounce of copper a little silver, with a view to making the color uniform. Then throw into the crucible again a small amount of salt. You will thus have a very fine *asem* [alloy].

Antimony

➤ THE FOLLOWING extract is from one of the more remarkable examples of chemical literature. Basil Valentine distinguished antimony from arsenic (the "poysonous" part) and recommended the compounds of antimony as medicines. He is one of a group of early chemists who, in emerging from the stage of alchemy, were still handicapped by the atmosphere of mystery and suspicion with which the "adepts of the art" surrounded themselves.

[2] By this operation, orpiment or sulfide of arsenic is slowly oxidized, in such a way as to change it into arsenious acid. We see that the latter is here called by the name of white alum.

THE TRIUMPHANT CHARIOT OF ANTIMONY, *being a con-scientious discovery of the many real transcendent Excel-lencies included in that Mineral. Written by Basileus,[8] a Benedictine monke, faithfully Englished and published for the common good. By I. H. Oxon, London: Printed for W. S. and are to be sold by Samuel Thomson at the Bishop's Head in Pauls Church Yard, 1661.*

➜ HE THAT WILL write of Antimony, needs a great considera-tion and most ample minde, and various rules of its prepara-tion and assured end; wherein it may with profit be used, that so he may give a certain undoubtful testimony of what is good or what is evil, what helpful and what poysonous.

'Tis no small thing truly to search out Antimony, thereby to know its essence and, at length by dilligence and experience, to obtaine the knowledge of it, to take away its poyson, (so much cryed out against by the clamours of the vulgar) and by a bet-ter omen to transmute it into wholesome medicine. Many in-quirers or Anatomists have hunted some here, some there, and miserably handled, tormented, and crucified Antimony, in so much that 'tis both inexpressible and incredible. But (really) they have not found out, or accomplished any profitable opera-tion, wandring from the true end, propounding to themselves things that are false, and thereby shadowing their sight, from beeing able to discerne the mask.

Antimony may deservedly be compared (& also Mercury) to an infinite Circle, and painted with all sorts of colours, and by how much the more it is sought into, so much the more is found out and learned, (so that your progresse therein be right and true.) In a word, one man's life is too too short, perfectly to be acquainted with its mysteries.

It is the worst of Poysons, the which being separated there-from, it becomes the supremest medicine, and is to be adminis-tered for inward and outward diseases. Which to many minds will seem incredible, and will be adjudged vanity and folly, but yet may be pardonable in them, because of their ignorance and want of judgment: but verily they are exceedingly to be blamed, who not knowing, have no desire after knowledge nor any will to learn.

Antimony hath four qualities, it is hot and cold, moist and dry, and imitates the four seasons of the year: it is also fixt and volatile: the volatile part is not void of poyson, but the fix'd part is altogether free there from.

---

[8] Basileus, who claimed to be a Benedictine monk, was one of the late alchemists, and was an upholder of the salt-sulphur-mercury doctrine. There is considerable mystery about him, as his name never appears in the records of members of the Benedictine order.

Bismuth

➤ BISMUTH, like arsenic and antimony, appeared in the list of known elements during the middle ages. It is not treated in "De Re Metallica," but Hoover inserted as a footnote in his translation the following account, taken from another of Agricola's works.

"De Re Metallica" was the first account of technical processes written by a layman who found the work of miners and metal workers interesting. It treats of a flourishing craft manned by highly skilled technicians who worked with a variety of metals.

GEORGIUS AGRICOLA[4] DE RE METALLICA. *Translated from the first Latin edition of 1556 by Herbert Clark Hoover and Lou Henry Hoover. Published for the Translators by The Mining Magazine, Salisbury House, London, 1912.*

➤ IN *Bermannus* [*Agricola*] says:

"*Bermannus.*—I will show you another kind of mineral which is numbered amongst metals, but appears to me to have been unknown to the Ancients; we call it *bisemutum*.

"*Naevius.*—Then in your opinion there are more kinds of metals than the seven commonly believed?

"*Bermannus.*—More, I consider; for this which just now I said we called *bisemutum*, cannot correctly be called *plumbum candidum* (tin) nor *nigrum* (lead), but is different from both, and is a third one. *Plumbum candidum* is whiter and *plumbum nigrum* is darker as you see.

"*Naevius.*—We see that this is of the color of *galena*.

"*Ancon.*—How then can *bisemutum*, as you call it, be distinguished from *galena*?

"*Bermannus.*—Easily; when you take it in your hands it stains them with black unless it is quite hard. The hard kind is not friable like galena, but can be cut. It is blacker than the kind of crude silver which we say is almost the colour of lead, and thus is different from both. Indeed, it not rarely contains some silver. It generally shows that there is silver beneath the place where it is found, and because of this our miners are accustomed to call it the 'roof of silver.' They are wont to roast this mineral, and from the better part they make metal; from the poorer part they make a pigment of a kind not to be despised."

This pigment was cobalt blue, indicating a considerable confusion of these minerals. This quotation is the first descrip-

[4] Agricola, who was not an alchemist at all, but a serious student of mining and metallurgy, wrote several books besides the famous "De Re Metallica," among them the "Bermannus," from which this description of bismuth ore is taken. The "Probierbüchlein" and "Nutliche Bergbüchlein" to which Mr. Hoover refers were anonymous handbooks for miners, in wide circulation in Agricola's day.

tion of bismuth, and the above text the first description of bismuth treatment. There is, however, bare mention of the mineral earlier, in the following single line from the *Probierbüchlein:* "Jupiter (controls) the ores of tin and *wismundt.*" And it is noted in the *Nütliche Bergbüchein* in association with silver.

The Oxygen Group

Group VIb

ELEMENT	ELECTRON SHELLS
$_8O$	$= K_2L_6$
$_{16}S$	$= K_2L_8M_6$
$_{34}Se$	$= K_2L_8M_{18}N_6$
$_{52}Te$	$= K_2L_8M_{18}N_{18}O_6$
$_{84}Po$	$= K_2L_8M_{18}N_{32}O_{18}P_6$

→SULFUR was one of the three mystic elements of the alchemists. Sulfuric acid is the key chemical in modern industry. Vapors from burning sulfur were known as fumigants from earliest times. Pliny the Elder, Roman scientist, wrote of deposits of the element around the volcanoes of Italy. He met his death from fumes from the volcanic eruption that buried Pompei and Herculaneum. Sulfur is the only ancient element in this group. Accounts of the others are given us by their discoverers, and are reprinted here.

Oxygen

LAVOISIER: ELEMENTS OF CHEMISTRY. *Translated from the French by Robert Kerr, 1790.*

→ I TOOK a matrass of about 36 cubical inches capacity, having a long neck, of six or seven lines internal diameter, and having bent the neck so as to allow of its being placed in the furnace, in such a manner that the extremity of its neck might be inserted under a bell-glass, placed in a trough of quicksilver; I introduced four ounces of pure mercury into the matrass, and, by means of a syphon, exhausted the air in the receiver, so as to raise the quicksilver, and I carefully marked the height at which it stood by pasting on a slip of paper. Having accurately noted the height of the thermometer and the barometer, I lighted a fire in the furnace, which I kept up almost continually during twelve days, so as to keep the quicksilver almost at its boiling point. Nothing remarkable took place during the first day: the mercury, though not boiling, was continually evaporating, and covered the interior surface of the vessels with small drops, at first very minute, which gradually augmenting to a sufficient size, fell back into the mass at the bottom of the vessel. On the second day, small red particles began to appear on the surface of the mercury which, during the four or five following days, gradually increased in size and number; after which they ceased to increase in either respect.

At the end of twelve days, feeling that the calcination of mercury did not at all increase, I extinguished the fire, and allowed the vessels to cool. The bulk of air in the body and neck of the matrass, and in the bell-glass, reduced to a medium of 28 inches of the barometer and 10° Reaumeur (54.5° Fahrenheit) of the thermometer, at the commencement of the experiment was about 50 cubical inches. At the end of the experiment the remaining air, reduced to the same medium pressure and temperature, was only between 42 and 43 cubical inches; consequently, it had lost about ⅙ of its bulk. Afterwards, having collected all the red particles, formed during the experiment, from the running mercury in which they floated, I found these to amount to 45 grains.

I was obliged to repeat this experiment several times, as it is difficult in one experiment both to preserve the whole air upon which we operate and to collect the whole of the red particles, or calx of mercury, which is formed during the calcination.

The air which remained after the calcination of the mercury in this experiment, and which was reduced to ⅚ of its former bulk, was no longer fit either for respiration or for combustion; animals being introduced into it were suffocated in a few seconds, and when a taper was plunged into it, it was extinguished as if it had been immersed into water.

In the next place, I took the 45 grains of red matter formed during this experiment, which I put into a small glass retort, having a proper apparatus for receiving such liquid, or gaseous product, as might be extracted: Having applied a fire to the retort in a furnace, I observed that, in proportion as the red matter became heated, the intensity of its color augmented. When the retort was almost red hot, the red matter began gradually to decrease in bulk, and in a few minutes after it disappeared altogether; at the same time 41½ grains of running mercury were collected in the recipient, and 7 or 8 cubical inches of elastic fluid, greatly more capable of supporting both respiration and combustion than atmospherical air, were collected in the bell-glass.

A part of this air being put into a glass tube of about an inch diameter, showed the following properties: A taper burned in it with a dazzling splendor, and charcoal, instead of consuming quietly as it does in common air, burnt with a flame, attended with a decrepitating noise, like phosphorus, and threw out such a brilliant light that the eyes could hardly endure it. This species of air was discovered almost at the same time by Mr. Priestley, Mr. Scheele, and myself. Mr. Priestley gave it the name of *dephlogisticated air*. Mr. Scheele called it *empyreal air*. At first I named it *highly respirable air*, to which has since been substituted the term *vital air*.

In reflecting upon the circumstances of this experiment, we readily perceive, that the mercury, during its calcination, absorbs the salubrious and respirable part of the air, or, to speak more strictly, the base of this respirable part; that the remaining air is a species of mephitis, incapable of supporting combustion or respiration; and consequently that atmospheric air is composed of two elastic fluids of different and opposite qualities. As a proof of this important truth, if we recombine these two elastic fluids which we have separately obtained in the above experiment, viz. the 42 cubical inches of mephitis, with the 8 cubical inches of respirable air, we reproduce an air precisely similar to that of the atmosphere, and possessing nearly the same power of supporting combustion and respiration, and of contributing to the calcination of metals.

Lavoisier's "vital air" is oxygen. "Phlogiston" became obsolete with this discovery, after dominating chemical thinking for a generation. Burning was believed by Scheele, Priestley and other chemists of the late eighteenth century to be a loss of phlogiston whereas it is actually a gain of oxygen.

Selenium

RECHERCHES SUR UN NOUVEAU CORPS MINÉRAL *trouvédans le soufre fabriqué à Fahlun. (Researches on a new mineral substance found in the sulfur refined at Fahlun.) Par. J. Berzelius. Annales de Chimie et de Physique, Vol. 9, (2nd series), Paris, 1818.*

→THE APPEARANCE of a substance as rare as tellurium in the sulfur of Fahlun engaged me in the task of isolating it, in order to have more accurate and more definite ideas about it. I therefore heated the entire mass which was found on the floor of the lead chamber. While moist it had a reddish color which, upon drying, became almost yellow. It weighed about four pounds. It was treated with nitro-muriatic acid added in quantity sufficient to make the mass pulpy, and it was then digested at a moderate heat. Little by little the color changed, the red disappeared, and the mass became greenish-yellow. After forty-eight hours of digestion, water and sulfuric acid were added and it was filtered. The liquid which passed through was a dark yellow. The mass left upon the filter was not visibly diminished in volume: it consisted principally of sulfur mixed with lead sulfate and other impurities. A small quantity of the liquid which had passed through was taken, in order to study the method of separating the substance presumed there; it was precipitated with ammonia. The precipitate, well washed and dried, mixed with potassium and heated at the bottom of a barometer tube, was decomposed by ignition. Thrown into water, a part of it was dissolved, and the liquid took on the orange color of strong beer, quite different from the wine-red given by potassium hydrotelluride. The liquid was scarcely covered by the silvery film which always forms on the surface of potassium hydrotelluride; but, after some hours, it became turbid, depositing red flocks, the quantity of which was increased by the addition of nitric acid. The precipitate was collected, and when a part of the filter which held the red precipitate was burned in a candle flame, it colored the flame azure blue, while giving off a very strong odor of rotten cabbage. A portion of very pure tellurium, precipitated in the same way from a solution of potassium hydrotelluride, had a gray color, gave a greenish color to the outer part of the flame, and produced a scarcely perceptible odor of radishes. On examining again the purified tellurium which had served in my old experiments on the oxide of tellurium and on gaseous hydrogen telluride, I found that it did not produce any odor, either when exposed to the blowpipe or when its oxide was reduced, and that the only way to make it produce such an odor was to heat it in a glass tube, closed by the finger, until the gasified metal blew a hole in the softened glass. It then burned through the hole with a blue flame, giving off an odor quite similar to that from the red substance.

These glass-blowing experiments proved to me that the red substance could scarcely be tellurium, but that the tellurium might contain something different, depending on whether it had been purified more or less.

Since the precipitate which I have just mentioned was scarcely considerable, I thought that the alkaline solution might have held some of it back; consequently I distilled it in a glass retort. That which distilled over at first was nothing but water; but when the mass began to solidify, it gave off a great quantity of gas which smelled strongly of rotten cabbage, but which could not be absorbed either by water or by a caustic solution, although it communicated its odor to the liquid through which it had passed. Moreover, the gas had the properties of nitrogen. In the receiver, a yellowish liquid condensed which contained sulfuric acid, and which was turbid with a brown powder. In the neck of the retort there had sublimed a saline mass almost black, and at the bottom there remained a small quantity of a yellowish salt, which became white on cooling.

The sulfuric solution in the receiver, filtered and heated to boiling to drive off the sulfuric acid, became cloudy again, depositing brown flocks, and lost its odor. The black salt, treated with water, left undissolved a brownish-black mass similar to that deposited in the liquid; the solution was colorless and contained a mixture of ammoniacal muriate and sulfite. . . .

The brown material insoluble in water, on closer examination, was recognized as the source of the particular odor which we mentioned above; and by the experiments of which we have given a sufficient account, it was found to be a combustible, elementary body, previously unknown, to which I have given the name of *selenium*, derived from selene (the moon), to recall its analogy with tellurium. From its chemical properties, this substance takes its place between sulfur and tellurium, although it has more properties in common with sulfur than with tellurium.

Tellurium

Abstract of a memoir of Klaproth, ON A NEW METAL DE-NOMINATED TELLURIUM. *Read at the Public Session of the Academy of Sciences at Berlin, January the 25th, 1798,** Nicholson's Journal, Vol. 2, 1798. ·

→KLAPROTH, the chemist of Berlin, in the chemical analysis of the auriferous ore, known by the name of the white ore of gold *(weiss golderz)*, aurum paradoxum, metallum vel aurum problematicum,† has discovered in that mineral, a metal absolutely different from all those which have hitherto been known, to which he has given the name of Tellurium, forming a kind of series or arrangement with the new metals discovered by him some time ago, and denominated Uranium and Ttitanium. Mr. Muller of Reichenstein, in the year 1782, had suspected the existence of a peculiar metallic substance, in this mineral. Bergman, to whom he had forwarded a specimen of the ore, confirmed his suspicion; but on account of the small quantity upon which he operated, he did not think fit to decide, whether this fossil did actually contain a new metal, or whether it might not be antimony which he had mistaken for a new product. . . .

1. Its color is white like tin, but inclining to a leaden grey. Its metallic splendor is considerable; its fracture lamellated. It is very brittle and friable, and by slow cooling it readily acquires a crystallized surface.

2. Its specific gravity is 6.115.

3. It belongs to the class of the most fusible metals. ·

* This abstract was communicated on the part of the author, by M. Rose, a chemist of Berlin, and was translated and forwarded to the Phylomatic Society at Paris, by L. Hecht the younger. The French translation, which of course I must follow (as the original is unpublished), is inserted in the XXVth vol. of the Annales de Chimie, p. 273.

† This mineral is found in the mine called *Mariahilf,* in the *Fatzbay* mountains near *Zalethna* in *Transilvania.*

4. Heated with the blow-pipe upon charcoal it burns with a flame considerably brilliant, of a blue color, but greenish at the edges, it rises totally in a grey whitish fume, and emits a disagreeable smell, which approaches that of radishes. If the flame be withdrawn before the small portion subjected to the heat is entirely volatilized, the remaining button preserves its fluid state for a long time, and, during the refrigeration, becomes covered with a radiated vegetation.

5. This metal amalgamates easily with mercury.

6. With sulfur it forms a sulfuret of a leaden-grey color, and radiated structure.

7. Its solution in the nitric acid is clear and colorless; when concentrated, it spontaneously, in the course of time, affords small white and light crystals in the form of needles, which possess the dendritic aggregation.

8. The new metal is likewise soluble in the nitro-muriatic acid: when a large quantity of water is added to a solution of this nature, the metal falls down in the state of oxide, in the form of a white powder, which in this state is soluble in the muriatic acid.

9. When a small quantity of this metal is mixed in the cold, with one hundred times its weight of concentrated sulfuric acid, in a closed vessel, the fluid gradually assumes a beautiful crimson red color. By the addition of a small quantity of water, added drop by drop, the color disappears, and the minute portion of metal which was dissolved falls down in the form of black flocks. Mere heat also destroys this solution; it causes the red color to disappear, and disposes the metal to separate in the state of a white oxide.

Polonium

Sur une Substance *nouvelle radioactive dans la pech-blende.* (On a new radio-active substance contained in pitchblend.) *Note de M. P. Curie et de Mme. S. Curie, présentée par M. Becquerel. Comptes rendus, Vol. 127, 1898.*

➔ Certain minerals containing uranium and thorium (pitchblend, chalcolite, uranite) are very active from the point of view of emission of Becquerel rays. In earlier work, one of us has shown that their activity is even greater than that of uranium and thorium, and has made the statement that this effect must be due to some other very active substance contained in a very small quantity in these minerals.

Study of the compounds of uranium and thorium has shown, in fact, that the property of emitting rays which make air a conductor and which register on photographic plates is a specific property of uranium and thorium which occurs in all the compounds of these metals, becoming weaker only as the proportion of the active metal in the compound is itself less. The physical state of these substances seems to be of entirely secondary importance. Various experiments have shown that the state of combination of substances seems to have effect only as it changes the proportion of active ingredients and the absorption produced by inert substances. Certain causes (such as the presence of impurities) which have such a strong effect on phosphorescence and fluorescence are here completely without action. It seems therefore very probable that if certain minerals are more active than uranium and thorium, that they contain a substance more active than these metals.

We have sought to isolate this substance in pitchblend, and experience has brought about confirmation of the foregoing predictions.

Our chemical researches have constantly been guided by the control of the radiant activity of the products separated in each operation. Each product is placed on one of the plates of a condenser, and the conductivity acquired by the air is measured with the aid of an electrometer and a piezo-electric quartz crystal, as cited in earlier work. This gives not only an indication but a numerical reading of the richness of the product in the active substance.

The pitchblend which we analyzed was about two and a half times as active as the uranium on the plates of our apparatus. We have attacked it with acids, and we have treated the resulting liquid with hydrogen sulfide. Uranium and thorium remain in the liquid. We recognize the following facts:

The precipitated sulfides contain a very active substance along with lead, bismuth, copper, arsenic and antimony.

This substance is completely insoluble in ammonium sulfate which separates it from arsenic and antimony.

The sulfides insoluble in ammonium sulfide were dissolved in nitric acid, the active substance perhaps incompletely separated from lead by sulfuric acid. On extracting the lead sulfate with dilute sulfuric acid, we succeed in dissolving in large part the active material precipitated with the lead sulfate.

The active substance is found in solution with bismuth and the copper is completely precipitated by ammonia, which separates it from the copper.

Finally the active material remains with the bismuth. . . .

We have sought whether there is any activity among substances actually known. We have examined compounds of nearly all the elements; thanks to the great kindness of many chemists, we have had samples of the rarest substances. Uranium and thorium are the only ones truly active, tantalum is perhaps very feebly so.

We believe therefore that the substance which we have recovered from pitchblend contains a metal not yet described, related to bismuth in its analytic properties. If the existence of this new metal is confirmed, we propose to call it *polonium*, after the native country of one of us.

The Halogen Group

Group VIIb

ELEMENT	ELECTRON SHELLS

$$_9F = K_2L_7$$
$$_{17}Cl = K_2L_8M_7$$
$$_{35}Br = K_2L_8M_{18}N_7$$
$$_{53}I = K_2L_8M_{18}N_{18}O_7$$
$$_{85}At = K_2L_8M_{18}N_{32}O_{18}P_7$$

Combining power is the outstanding characteristic of the halogen elements. A glance at the description of their electron shell structure will show how each of these elements needs but one electron to achieve the perfection of the closed shell structure. The properties of the elements are dramatic in the extreme. Fluorine sets fire to water. Chlorine was the original poison war gas. Bromine takes its name from its stench. Iodine, of the beautiful vapor, behaves in many remarkable ways due to its semi-metallic nature. Astatine is the product of radioactive decay of the man-made elements. If it ever existed naturally, that isotope has long ago vanished from the earth. Discoverers of these interesting chemicals tell here their first impressions of them.

Chlorine

ON MANGANESE, AND ITS PROPERTIES. *By Karl Wilhelm Scheele[1] (translated from "Om Brunsten, Eller Magnesia, och-dess Egenskaper," Kong. Vetenskaps Academiens Handlingar, XXXV, Stockholm, 1774). Reprinted from "The Early History of Chlorine," Alembic Club Reprints, No. 13, London, 1897.* ➤ IN ORDER clearly to apprehend this novelty I took a retort containing a mixture of manganese and *acidum salis*. In front of the neck I bound a bladder emptied of air, and set the retort in hot sand. The bladder became distended by the effervescence in the retort. When the acid no longer effervesced, which was an indication of its saturation, I removed the bladder, and

[1] Scheele's name was written various ways on different publications: Karl Wilhelm, Carl Wilhelm, Charles William, Charles Guillhaume. It was as given here on this publication.

found that this air had colored it yellow, as if by *aqua fortis*, but did not contain any trace of *aer fixus;* it had, however, a quite characteristically suffocating smell, which was most oppressive to the lungs. It resembled the smell of warm *aqua regis*. The solution in the retort was clear, inclining to yellow, which last mentioned color was caused by its containing iron. . . .

This marine acid, deprived of phlogiston as one of its constituents, unites with water in very small quantity; and gives the water a slightly acid taste; but as soon as it comes in contact with a combustible matter it becomes again a proper marine acid. In order to investigate the properties of this air it is best to put it to the test in the elastic state. Ordinary marine acid is mixed with finely-ground manganese, in any chosen quantity, in a glass retort which is placed on warm sand; small bottles which hold about twelve ounces of water are employed as receivers; about two drachms of water are put into each bottle, and the joints are not luted except by means of gray paper wrapped round the neck of the retort, and on this the bottle is fixed. When a bottle has remained a quarter of an hour or more, it is found, according to the quantity of the elastic acid in the receiver, that the air in it assumes a yellow color; the bottle is then removed from the retort. . . .

Whatever was experimented with in this dephlogisticated marine acid was hung on a glass tube which I fastened into the cork.

(a) The corks in the bottles became yellow, as from *aqua fortis,* and during the distillation the luting was likewise attacked.

(b) Blue litmus paper became almost white; all vegetable flowers—red, blue, and yellow—became white in a short time; the same thing also occurred with green plants. In the meantime the water in the bottle became changed to a weak and pure marine acid.

(c) The former colors of these flowers, as well as those of the green plants, could not be restored either by alkalies or by acids.

(d) Expressed oils and animal fats, when they hung as drops on the glass tube or were rubbed on it, became in a short time tough like turpentine.

(e) Cinnabar became white on the surface, and when the piece was washed in water a pure *mercurius sublimatus* solution was obtained, but the sulfur was not altered.

(f) Iron vitriol became red, and deliquesced. Copper and zinc vitriols were unaltered.

(g) Iron filings were put into the same bottle and they dissolved. This solution was evaporated *ad siccum* and distilled with addition of oil of vitriol, when a pure marine acid, which did not dissolve gold, again passed over.

(h) All metals were attacked, and with gold it is noteworthy that its solution in this dephlogisticated marine acid forms with *alkali volatile* an *aurum fulminans*.

(*i*) When *spiritus salis ammoniaci,* prepared with lime, hung in drops on the tube, there arose a white cloud, and a quantity of air bubbles escaped from the drops, which gave off a smoke when they burst asunder.

(*k*) *Alkali fixum* was changed into *sal commune* which decrepitated on charcoal, but did not detonate.

(*l*) Arsenic deliquesced in these vapors. (*m*) Insects immediately died in them. (*n*) And fire was immediately extinguished by them.

Bromine

Memoire sur une SUBSTANCE PARTICULIERE CONTENUE DANS L'EAU DE LA MER. (*Memoir on an unusual substance contained in sea water*). *Par M. Balard, Annales de Chimie et de Physique, Series 2, Vol 32, Paris, 1826.*

→ I HAVE noticed many times that, upon treating with an aqueous solution of chlorine the extract of kelp ash which contains iodine, after adding a solution of starch there appears, not only the blue zone formed with iodine, but also, a little above it, a zone of a fairly intense yellow tint.

This orange-yellow color appeared also when I treated the mother-liquor from our salt-works in the same manner; and the tint became deeper as the liquid became more concentrated. The appearance of this color is accompanied by a peculiar sharp odor.

I tried to find what could be the nature of this coloring principle, and my first attempts in this direction lead me to the following observations:

1. The mother-liquor of the brine, treated with chlorine, loses its color and its characteristic odor after being exposed for one or two days to contact with the air, without the chlorine being able afterward to reproduce the same phenomena in it;

2. If it is treated with alkalis or alkaline sub-carbonates, the odor and color are equally removed;

3. The same effects are produced when a reagent which will yield hydrogen, either itself or with the aid of water, is added to the colored liquid.

This is accomplished by sulfuric acid, ammonia, hydrogen sulfide, the hydro-sulfates, but especially by a mixture of zinc and sulfuric acid which introduces into the liquid hydrogen in the nascent state;

4. In the case where the decoloration is the result of alkalis or hydrogenated bodies, the addition of chlorine can re-establish the original color.

Two interpretations come to mind naturally to explain these various phenomena.

In the first place, it may be supposed that the yellow material may be a combination of chlorine with some of the
materials contained in the mother liquor of the brine.

It could be admitted, in the second place, that the coloring
substance had been liberated from one of its compounds by
chlorine, which has taken its place.

In order to know which to believe, it was indispensible to
get the coloring material in the isolated state. Its volatility
seemed to give hope that distillation would be enough to
separate it from the solution, and I had recourse to that
procedure. . . .

The conjecture which I considered the most plausible concerning the nature of this red substance which was recovered
from the brine, following the action of chlorine, and to which
I turned my attention, brought with it the necessity for giving
it a name which would allow it to be followed easily through
its compounds, and which, freeing me from having recourse
to such terms as *the red material, the substance set free by
chlorine, etc.*, necessarily embarrassing, would lend itself to
representing with greater fidelity the opinion which I had conceived concerning it.

I had recourse to the advice of the learned professor whose
pupil I have the honor to be, and whose wise counsel has
directed my inexperience in the course of this work, carried
out under his supervision.

I owe it to his advice and to the inspiration which he has
given me that I have overcome obstacles which interfered
with my researches, and I am glad to tender him my recognition here.

M. Anglada advised me to call this substance *Bromine*, de-
riving the name from the Greek βρωμος (fœtor). This name
lends itself wonderfully well to the formation of the compound
expressions made necessary by its combinations, and I have
adopted it for simplicity of expression.

If the chemists confirm the results which I believe I have
caught sight of, if they assure definitely to this substance a
place among the elements, I think that this name ought to be
maintained.

Iodine

DÉCOUVERTE D'UNE SUBSTANCE NOUVELLE DANS LE VARECK
(*Discovery of a new substance in kelp.*) *Par M. B. Courtois.
Annales de Chimie, Series 1, Vol. 88, Paris, 1813.*

➤ THE MOTHER-LIQUOR from leaching of kelp contains a
fairly large quantity of a very unusual and remarkable substance; it may be extracted easily: just pour sulfuric acid into
the mother-liquor and heat in a retort whose neck is fitted
to a condenser and that to a flask. The substance which is pre-

cipitated in the form of a shining black powder, immediately after the addition of sulfuric acid, rises in vapor of a superb violet color when it is heated; this vapor congeals in the condenser and in the receiver, in the form of very brilliant crystalline plates with a luster equal to that of crystallized lead sulfide; on washing these plates with a little distilled water, the substance is obtained in the pure state.

The beautiful color of the vapor of this material is sufficient to distinguish it from everything known up to the present; but it has many other remarkable properties, which make this discovery very interesting.

This is due to M. Courtois, the saltpeter supplier in Paris, who sent some to Messrs. Désormes and Clément, about 18 months ago, upon their promising to follow up the researches which he had begun. Here are the results:

The new substance, which has since been named *iodine* on account of the beautiful violet color of its vapor, has every appearance of a metal. Its specific gravity is about four times that of water. It is very volatile; its odor is similar to that of oxymuriatic gas; it stains paper and the hands a reddish-brown, but these stains disappear after a little time; it is neither acid nor alkaline; on putting it into a retort and heating, it volatilizes at a very moderate heat, about 75° centigrade. If water into which it has been put is heated, it is possible to see the substance boil under the water and produce the vapor of a magnificent violet color; on subliming a considerable quantity, there are obtained very brilliant and fairly large plates, but they do not solidify; it is a little soluble in water, more so in alcohol, and very much so in ether. . . .

Fluorine

ACTION D'UN COURANT *électrique sur l'acide flourhydrique anhydride (Action of an electric current on anhydrous hydrofluoric acid). Note de M. H. Moissan, présentée per M. Debray. Comptes rendus, Vol. 102, Paris, 1886.*

→ BY SUBMITTING to electrolysis, by means of current from a 50-element Bunsen battery, in a platinum U-tube, anhydrous hydrofluoric acid prepared by the process of M. Fremy, with all the precautions indicated by that scientist, there was obtained, on operating it at —50°:

At the negative pole: liberation of hydrogen, easily recognized.

At the positive pole: a continuous current of a gas showing the following properties: in the presence of mercury, complete absorption with formation of protofluoride of mercury, of a clear yellow color; in contact with water, decomposition of this last with production of ozone.

Phosphorus takes fire in the presence of this gas, giving phosphorus fluoride. Sulfur heats up and melts rapidly. Carbon seems to be without action. Fused potassium chloride is attacked in the cold with liberation of chlorine.

Finally crystallized silicon, which has been washed with nitric acid and with hydrofluoric acid, takes fire on contact with this gas and burns explosively, producing silicon fluoride.

The platinum and iridium electrode forming the positve pole is strongly corroded, while the platinum electrode of the negative pole is intact.

I cannot draw definite conclusions[1] from this action of the current on hydrofluoric acid; I can only point out preliminary results today; I am continuing these researches and I hope soon to submit new experiments on the subject for the judgment of the Academy.

Astatine

SOME CHEMICAL PROPERTIES OF ELEMENT 85. *By E. Segrè, K. R. Mackenzie and D. R. Corson, in Physical Review, 2nd series, Vol. 57, 1940.*

➤THE CHEMICAL identification of element 85 is made on the basis of the following evidence: The activity can be easily separated from mercury, lead, thallium, bismuth and polonium $(80 < Z < 84)$ by various reactions.

The possibility that the new substance be a fission product is ruled out by physicial arguments as well as by chemical evidence. Among its chemical properties we mention: It is precipitated by hydrogen sulfide in six normal hydrochloric acid solution with various carriers, and the sulfide is insoluble in ammonium sulfide; it is precipitated by stannous chloride in acid solution but not by sodium stannite in alkaline solution; it is volatile at comparatively low temperatures; a piece of bombarded bismuth loses most of the activity before melting (275°).

The general behavior of element 85 is that of a metal, and in the usual scheme of analysis would go in the hydrogen sulfide group. It shows little resemblance to the other halogens. For example, in dilute nitric solution it does not precipitate with silver nitrate using iodide as a carrier. It can be distilled from dilute nitric acid solution or extracted with carbon tetrachloride but with yields very small compared with iodine under similar conditions. Dr. J. G. Hamilton has shown that element 85 is concentrated in the thyroid.

[1] Various hypotheses might be made concerning the nature of the gas liberated, the simplest would be that we are in the presence of fluorine, but it might be possible, for example, that this is a perfluoride of hydrogen or even a mixture of hydrofluoric acid and ozone active enough to explain such energetic action as this gas has upon crystallized silicon.

The Inert Gases

Group O

ELEMENT	ELECTRON SHELLS
$_2He$	$= K_2$
$_{10}Ne$	$= K_2L_8$
$_{18}A$	$= K_2L_8M_8$
$_{36}Kr$	$= K_2L_8M_{18}N_8$
$_{54}Xe$	$= K_2L_8M_{18}N_{18}O_8$
$_{86}Rn$	$= K_2L_8M_{18}N_{32}O_{18}P_8$

Helium

HELIUM: *Its History, Properties, and Commercial Development. By Richard B. Moore, in Journal of the Franklin Institute, Philadelphia, Pa. Vol. 191, 1921.*

→ THE STORY of helium is one of the romances of science. There is probably nothing, unless it be the story of radium, which can compete with it in human interest. It represents one of the very best examples of a discovery in pure science which ultimately has a great commercial application.

In 1868 there was an eclipse of the sun which was visible in India. A number of scientific men were in India at the time making observations of the eclipse, and a spectroscope was for the first time turned on the solar chromosphere, that portion of the atmosphere of the sun, about ten miles deep, which merges into the corona. A bright yellow line was observed which was at first thought to be the sodium line. Janssen, however, showed that this line was not exactly the same as the D_1 and D_2 lines of sodium, although extremely close to these lines. He, therefore, suggested that the line have the designation D_3. Frankland and Lockyer decided that this line was due to a new element in the sun which had not previously been discovered on the earth and they suggested the name "Helium," from the Greek word "Hellios," meaning the sun.

For a great many years nothing more was done in connection with this element. In 1888, Dr. W. F. Hillebrand, of the United States Geological Survey, examined the gases which were evolved from certain uraninites when boiled with dilute sulfuric acid. Hillebrand obtained an inert gas which showed all of the properties of nitrogen. When sparked with hydrogen, in presence of hydrochloric acid, it gave ammonium chloride, and when sparked with oxygen, it gave oxides of nitrogen. On the other hand, it was noticed that there were some lines in this spectrum which did not belong to nitrogen, and, in addition, after continuous sparking for a considerable period, there was a residue which diminished in volume very slowly. It is a great pity that American science was not responsible for the discovery of terrestrial helium. On the other hand, those who have worked with the rare gases can fully appreciate the difficulties attendant on work of this kind before the necessary technic was even partially developed.

In 1894, Sir William Ramsay, in conjunction with Lord Rayleigh, made his memorable discovery of argon in the atmosphere, which discovery was announced at the British Association Meeting in the same year. After this discovery, Ramsay looked for other sources of the element. He heard through Sir Henry Miers of the observation of Doctor Hillebrand, described above, and suspected that the inert gas found by Hillebrand might be argon. He obtained a sample of the mineral cleveite from Doctor Hillebrand, placed it in a tube connected with a Töpler pump, heated the mineral with sulfuric acid, pumped off the evolved gas, sparked the latter with oxygen, removed the excess of oxygen, and finally ran the purified gas into a spectrum tube. The spectrum was entirely different from that of argon, having as a chief characteristic a bright yellow line. Sir William once described to the writer, in his characteristic manner, his surprise at what he saw when he put his small spectroscope to his eye. He was expecting to see the argon spectrum, consisting of lines more or less evenly distributed across the whole field of the instrument, or at least the bands of nitrogen. Instead, he observed a very brilliant yellow line, with two or three fainter reds, as many greens, and as many violets. These were more or less masked by slight impurities in the gas. His surprise was so great that he thought at first there was something wrong with his spectroscope, and took out his handkerchief and mechanically wiped the prism. Others were called in who suggested various explanations for the bright yellow line, the most common being that it was the sodium line due to dirty electrodes or other causes. It was only when the spectrum of the sodium flame was compared with the yellow line from the spectrum tube that it became evident, and beyond question, that a new element—terrestrial helium—had been discovered. The wave-length was measured by Sir William Crookes and proved to coincide with that of the D_3 solar line.

The discovery of argon, followed by the discovery of helium, was the forerunner of the series of brilliant researches by

Ramsay and Travers, which gave to the world five new elements, commonly called rare gases of the atmosphere, namely, helium, neon, argon, krypton, and xenon.

Argon

THE RECENTLY DISCOVERED GASES AND THEIR RELATION TO THE PERIODIC LAW. *By William Ramsay. An address delivered before the Deutschen chemischen Gesellschaft, December 19, 1898. Translated by "J.L.H." Printed in Science, 1899.*

→ IT IS well known to you how the remarkable observation of Lord Rayleigh that nitrogen from the atmosphere possesses a greater density than that prepared from ammonia or nitrates led to the discovery of argon, a new constituent of the air. I need not say that had it not been for this observation the investigations of which I shall speak this evening would never have been carried out, at least not by me. You also, doubtless, will remember that the search for some compound of argon was rewarded, not by the attainment of the quest, but by the discovery, in cleveite and other rare uranium minerals, of helium, an element whose existence in the chromosphere of the sun had already been suspected. And, further, I hardly need recall to your minds that the density of helium is in round numbers 2, and that of argon 20, and that the ratio of specific heats of both these gases, unlike that of most others, is 1.66.

From these figures it follows that the atomic weight of helium is 4 and that of argon 40. It is true that in many quarters this conclusion is not admitted, but I have always thought it better to recognize the validity of the theory of gases and accept the logical deductions than to deny the truth of the present theories. The only reason for not admitting the correctness of these atomic weights is that that of argon is greater than that of potassium, but this is no severer attack upon the validity of the periodic law than the accepted position of iodin after, instead of before, tellurium. As a matter of fact, all the more recent determinations of the atomic weight of tellurium give the figure 127.6, while that of iodine remains unchanged at 127.

Since these new elements form no compounds, it is not possible to decide the question by purely chemical methods. Were it only possible for us to prepare a single volatile compound of helium or of argon our problem would be solved. In spite of many attempts, I have not been able to confirm Berthelot's results with benzine or carbon bisulfide. I have, however, offered to place a liter of argon at the disposal of my distinguished colleague, that he may repeat his experiments on a larger scale. No one can doubt that it is exceedingly desirable that the question of these atomic weights should be finally decided, and that by chemical methods.

Dr. Hampson, the inventor of a very simple and practical machine for the preparation of liquid air, which is based upon the same principle as that of Herr Linde, was so kind as to place large quantities of liquid air at my disposal. In order to become acquainted with the art of working with so unusual a material, I asked Dr. Hampson for a liter; with this Dr. Travers and I practiced and made different little experiments to prepare ourselves for the great experiment of liquefying argon.

Krypton

It seemed to me a pity to boil away the air without collecting the last residue; for, though it seemed improbable that the looked-for element could be here, yet it was, indeed, possible that a heavier gas might accompany the argon. This suspicion was confirmed. The residue from the liquid air consisted chiefly of oxygen and argon, and, after removing the oxygen and nitrogen, beside the spectrum of argon were two brilliant lines, one in the yellow, which was not identical with D_3 of helium, and one in the green. This gas was decidedly heavier than argon; its density was 22.5 instead of the 20 of argon. We had, therefore, discovered a new body, which was an element, for the ratio between the specific heats was 1.66. To this element we gave the name "krypton." Up to this time we have not followed further the study of this element; we have, however, collected and preserved many residues which are rich in krypton. It was our first intention to examine the lightest part of the argon. In many, however, we marked, in passing, that the wavelength of the green line of krypton is exceedingly close to that of the northern lights, being 5,570, while the latter is 5,571.

Our whole supply of argon was now liquefied in the following manner: The gasometer containing the argon was connected with a series of tubes in which the gas passed over respectively hot copper oxid, concentrated sulfuric acid, and phosphorous pentoxid; it then passed by a two-way cock into a small flask, holding about 30 cubic centimeters, which was enclosed in a Dewar tube. By means of the other opening of the cock, the flask was connected with a mercury gasometer. By means of a U-shaped capillary and mercury trough, it was also possible, through a three-way cock, to collect the gas at will in glass tubes. About 50 cubic centimeters of liquid air were poured into the double walled tube, and, by means of a

Fleuss air pump kept constantly in action, the liquid air boiled at 10 to 15 millimeters pressure. The argon liquefied rapidly as soon as subjected to this low temperature, and in the course of half an hour it was completely condensed. Altogether there were about 25 cubic centimeters of a clear, limpid, colorless liquid, in which floated white flakes of a solid substance. By stopping the pump the pressure over the liquid air was now increased, and the argon boiled quietly, the first portions of the gas being collected in the mercury gasometer. Changing now the three-way cock, the largest portion of the argon passed back into the iron gasometer; after nearly all the liquid had boiled away and only the solid substance was left in the flask, the last portions of the gas were collected separately. The solid substance remained persistently in the flask; it was slowly volatilized by means of a Töpler pump, which stood in connection with the apparatus.

We first directed our attention to the lighter fractions, for these had for us the greatest interest. The density of this gas was found to be 14.67; the ratio between the specific heats was as usual 1.66 and the spectrum showed, beside the well-known groupings of argon, a large number of red, orange, and yellow lines of varying intensity. Evidently we had before us a new element, which was contaminated with argon.

Neon

This gas was then liquefied in a similar apparatus to that first used, but constructed on a smaller scale; a portion, however, remained uncondensed. Even by raising the reservoir of the mercury gasometer until an overpressure of an atmosphere was reached, it was impossible to convert all the gas into a liquid, although the temperature of the boiling air was reduced as low as possible by rapid pumping. By repeated raising and lowering of the reservoir we finally passed all the gas through the cooled space, in order to free it, as far as possible, from argon. The uncondensible gas was collected by itself, and the remainder was evaporated into another gasometer.

You can well imagine how eager we were to know what the density of this purified gas would prove to be. It was immediately weighed. Our satisfaction can well be realized when we found that its density was 9.76. Since, however, its spectrum at low pressure still showed argon lines, though weak, we were compelled to admit that this number was certainly too high. It was impossible that this gas should not contain argon, since at the temperature used argon possessed a measurable vapor pressure.

We have, therefore, estimated that the density of the pure

gas is 9.65. Here our work for the time was ended by the beginning of the summer holidays.

On our return we resumed the study of this gas, which we will hereafter designate by its name of "neon." Its spectrum was photographed by Mr. Baly, one of my assistants, by means of a spectrometer which we had constructed during the vacation. To our astonishment, the lines of helium were easily recognized. A comparison photograph showed this beyond all question. Hence the density of the gas was in all probability too low, owing to the presence of the helium. Since now the temperature used was insufficient to liquefy the neon, and since the argon had been removed as far as possible, we had to face the problem of how one could free neon from its accompanying impurities. A means was found in its solubility. It is well known that the solubility of those gases which do not react chemically with the solvent follows in general the same order as their condensibility. According to this helium should have a lesser solubility than neon, and neon than argon. The solubility of these gases in water is, however, too slight to be available for their separation. We have, therefore, used liquid oxygen as a solvent. This mixes with all three gases and boils at a temperature not far from the boiling point of argon. We therefore mixed the gas with sufficient oxygen to be almost wholly condensed at the temperature attained by boiling air at the lowest possible pressure. The uncondensed portion, about one-fifth of the whole, was separated and collected as that richest in helium; the middle portion we considered as purified neon, while the remainder consisted of a mixture of argon and neon; naturally, all these portions contained oxygen in larger or smaller quantities.

After the removal of the oxygen, which was accomplished by passage over hot copper filings, we determined the density and refractivity of the middle portion. The density in two determinations was 10.04 and 10.19; the second figure was obtained after passing the electric spark through the gas mixed with oxygen in the presence of caustic potash and subsequent removal of the oxygen by phosphorus. The entire quantity weighed was only 30 cubic centimeters at a pressure of 250 millimeters. The weight was 0.0095 gram. I mention these figures in order to show with what an exceedingly small quantity of gas it is possible to carry out a very satisfactory density determination.

As regards krypton, which is distinguished by three brilliant lines, one in red, one in yellow and one in green, we are in much the same position. We have collected a considerable quantity of the impure gas, which shows the spectrum finely, although that of argon is also present. We hope that we shall soon be able to pursue this portion of our work further. We can merely note here that the specific gravity of the gas which shows this spectrum in such a marked way is not far different from that of argon.

Xenon

The heaviest of these gases we have weighed, although in impure condition. Its density is 32.5. I need not call your attention to the fact that there is space for an element of the helium group between bromin and rubidium. Such an element should have an atomic weight of 81 to 83, which corresponds to a density of 40.5 to 41.5, under the very probable supposition that, like the other gases of this group, it is mon-atomic. The spectrum of this gas, which we have named "xenon"—the stranger—has many lines; none of these are of marked intensity, and in this respect the spectrum resembles somewhat that of argon. It is also analogous to argon in another particular, that the spectrum undergoes a remarkable change when a Leyden jar is put into the circuit. As with argon, many new blue and green lines appear, while other lines, mostly in the red, either disappear or lose much of their intensity. Further than this we have not proceeded in studying xenon; for our attention has been given chiefly to neon, as well as to a problem regarding argon.

Radon (Emanation)

THE INTERPRETATION OF RADIUM AND THE STRUCTURE OF THE ATOM. *By Frederick Soddy, New York, 1922.*

➤IF THIS SPECIMEN of radium bromide was dissolved in water and the liquid evaporated down to dryness in order to get back the solid compound, it would be found that as the result of this very simple operation the radium had lost the greater part of its radioactivity in the process. The penetrating β- and γ-rays would have completely disappeared, and the non-penetrating X-rays would only be one quarter as powerful as initially. Then a strange thing would happen. Left to itself the radium would spontaneously *recover* its lost activity, little by little from day to day, and at the end of a month it would not be appreciably less active than it at first was, or as it now is. This appears to be in direct conflict with the statement previously made that the radioactivity of radium cannot be affected by any known process, but it is only apparently so. If we study the process carefully we shall find that when the radium is dissolved in water "something" escapes into the air, and this "something" is intensely radioactive. It diffuses about in the air, but remains contained within a closed vessel, if it is gas-tight. In short, this "something" is a new *gas* possessing the property of radioactivity to a very intense degree.

We owe the greater part of our knowledge of this new radio-active gas to Sir Ernest Rutherford, who has given to it a special name. He called it the *emanation of radium,* or, for short, simply the *emanation.* The vague term "emanation" is, with our present exact knowledge of its real nature, apt to mislead. Some, unfortunately, have used the term "emanation" or "emanations" in speaking of the various *radiations* which radium emits, and which we have already considered in some detail. Sir William Ramsay has proposed the name "Niton" for this new gas, in order to emphasize its relationship to the other argon gases. However, as similar new gases or emanations are given by two other of the radioactive elements, thorium and actinium, the original term has been generally retained. The term "emanation," qualified when necessary by the name of the radioactive element producing it, denotes one of these new gaseous bodies, and it is necessary not to confuse this particular use with its older and more general uses. . . .

It has even been found possible to settle the chemical nature of this new gas, and to place it in its proper family of elements in the periodic table. Almost all gases, according to their various natures, are absorbed when subjected to the action of various chemical reagents. Thus oxygen is absorbed by phosphorus, hydrogen by heated copper oxide, nitrogen by heated magnesium, and so on. The exceptions, namely, gases which are not absorbed by any reagents and which will not combine with anything, are the newly discovered gases of Lord Rayleigh and Sir William Ramsay—argon, helium, neon, etc.—which exist in atmospheric air. The quantity in the air of these gases is extremely minute except in the single case of argon, which is present to the extent of one per cent. The radium emanation, like argon, is not absorbed by any known reagent, and does not appear to possess any power of chemical combination. It may be passed unchanged through absorbents, or subjected to drastic chemical treatment which would suffice to absorb every known gas except those of the argon type, and the conclusion has been arrived at that the emanation is an element of the same family nature as the argon gases. Like them, it exists in the form of single atoms—that is, its molecule is monatomic. Radium, on the other hand, in its chemical nature is extremely similar to barium, strontium, and calcium, a family known as the alkaline-earth elements. None other of the argon elements or the alkaline-earth elements are radioactive, and yet the radioactive elements are quite normal in their chemical properties, closely resembling ordinary elements, and being associated in the clearest and closest way with one or another of the old well-known types or families. More recently, by using quantities of radium about fifteen times as great as those used tonight in our experiments, it has been possible to photograph its spectrum. This proves to be a new and characteristic bright-line spectrum, resembling in general character the spectra of the other argon gases, but absolutely distinct.

It has been found possible to obtain some idea of the density of the emanation of radium, and therefore of the weight of its atom, from experiments on the rate of its diffusion from one place to another. These indicate that the gas is extremely dense —denser probably than mercury vapour—and therefore that it has a very heavy atom. Finally, by means of a new special micro-balance thousands of times more sensitive than the most delicately constructed chemist's balance, the emanation has actually been weighed by Sir William Ramsay and Mr. Whytlaw-Gray. These experiments and the whole of the available evidence agree in indicating that the atomic weight of the emanation is 222, which is four units below that of radium, and therefore is the fourth heaviest known.

The heavy, inert gas, element 86, has many names. "Niton" gave way to "Radon." The isotope derived from thorium was then named "Thoron" and that from actinium "Acton." The term "Emanation" (symbol Em) is now coming back into use, summing up the isotopes.

PARTICLES RESEMBLING GASES:—A gas consists of freely moving particles. Electrons carrying a current through metal are found to move similarly, so physicists speak of an "electron gas." Electrons spin, and obey Fermi-Dirac statistics like material particles (Pauli exclusion principle). The term "photon gas" is used to describe radiation phenomena. Bose-Einstein statistics describe the motion of these non-material units of radiation.

The Neutron

The Neutron Predicted

From Aston's discoveries with a primitive form of the mass spectrograph, Rutherford postulated the structure of the atomic nucleus as a close combination of electrons with hydrogen nuclei. He predicted the discovery of the neutron, of deuterium and of the two particles of mass 3; tritium, an isotope of hydrogen, and He³. To put Rutherford's descriptions into modern phraseology, read "neutron" for each pair consisting of hydrogen nucleus and tightly bound electron, and "proton" for each hydrogen nucleus without the electron. The quotation below is but a part of the lecture.

NUCLEAR CONSTITUTION OF ATOMS, *Bakerian Lecture by Sir E. Rutherford, Proc. Roy. Soc., 1920.*

→IN CONSIDERING the possible constitution of the elements, it is natural to suppose that they are built up ultimately of hydrogen nuclei and electrons. On this view the helium nucleus is composed of four hydrogen nuclei and two negative electrons with a resultant charge of two. The fact that the mass of the helium atom 3.997 in terms of oxygen 16 is less than the mass of four hydrogen atoms, viz., 4.032, has been generally supposed to be due to the close interaction of the fields in the nucleus, resulting in a smaller electromagnetic mass than the sum of the masses of the individual components.

Sommerfield has concluded from this fact that the helium nucleus must be a very stable structure which would require intense forces to disrupt it. Such a conclusion is in agreement with experiment, for no evidence has been obtained to show that helium can be disintegrated by the swift a particles which are able to disrupt the nuclei of nitrogen and oxygen.

In his recent experiments on the isotopes of ordinary elements, Aston* has shown that within the limit of experimental accuracy the masses of all the isotopes examined are given by whole numbers when oxygen is taken as 16. The only exception is hydrogen, which has a mass 1.008 in agreement with chemical observations. This does not exclude the probability that hydrogen is the ultimate constituent of which nuclei are composed, but indicates that either the grouping of the hydrogen nuclei and electrons is such that the average electromagnetic mass is nearly 1, or, what is more probable, that the secondary units, of which the atom is mainly built up, *e.g.*, helium or its isotope, have a mass given nearly by a whole number when oxygen is 16.

The experimental observations made so far are unable to settle whether the new atom (Helium 3) has a mass exactly 3, but from analogy with helium we may expect the nucleus of the new atom to consist of three H nuclei and one electron, and to have a mass more nearly 3 than the sum of the individual masses in the free state.

Deuterium

If we are correct in this assumption it seems very likely that one electron can also bind two H nuclei and possibly also one H nucleus. In the one case, this entails the possible existence of an atom nearly 2 carrying one charge, which is to be regarded as an isotope of hydrogen. In the other case, it involves the idea of the possible existence of an atom of mass 1 which has zero nucleus charge.

Neutron

Such an atomic structure seems by no means impossible. On present views, the neutral hydrogen atom is regarded as a nucleus of unit charge with an electron attached at a distance, and the spectrum of hydrogen is ascribed to the movements of this distant electron. Under some conditions, however, it may be possible for an electron to combine much more closely with the H nucleus, forming a kind of neutral doublet.

* Phil. Mag. Dec., 1919; April and May, 1920.

Such an atom would have very novel properties. Its external field would be practically zero, except very close to the nucleus, and in consequence it should be able to move freely through matter. Its presence would probably be difficult to detect by the spectroscope, and it may be impossible to contain it in a sealed vessel. On the other hand, it should enter readily the structure of atoms, and may either unite with the nucleus or be disintegrated by its intense field, resulting possibly in the escape of a charged H atom or an electron or both.

If the existence of such atoms be possible, it is to be expected that they may be produced, but probably only in very small numbers, in the electric discharge through hydrogen, where both electrons and H nuclei are present in considerable numbers. It is the intention of the writer to make experiments to test whether any indication of the production of such atoms can be obtained under these conditions.

The existence of such nuclei may not be confined to mass 1 but may be possible for masses 2, 3, or 4, or more, depending on the possibility of combination between the doublets. The existence of such atoms seems almost necessary to explain the building up of the nuclei of heavy elements; for unless we suppose the production of charged particles of very high velocities it is difficult to see how any positively charged particle can reach the nucleus of a heavy atom against its intense repulsive field.

We have seen that so far the nuclei of three light atoms have been recognized experimentally as probable units of atomic structure, viz.,

$$H_1^+ \qquad X_3^{++} \qquad He_4^{++}$$

where the subscript represents the mass of the element.

The actual neutron was discovered by J. Chadwick in England in 1932.

The Metals

➤ FOLLOWING the first two "short periods" in the Periodic Table there begins, after Group III, the long series of elements which are useful primarily for their metallic qualities. In some of the most recent forms of the Table these are placed in one long line, joining the elements known for their alkaline qualities, written at the left, and the more acidic ones, ending with the halogens, at the right. The in-between metals are sometimes referred to as the "transition" elements, although that name can be applied to almost any series, because of the gradual change in chemical properties from each group to the next.

In the familiar arrangement of the Table there is, however, the advantage of seeing the elements grouped according to their characteristic valencies. In the following accounts of these metals, they will be taken up according to this method of classification, beginning with the "noble" metals of Group I., and stressing the "family" traits.

Some of these metals were known before the beginning of written history. Some are so new that no satisfactory sample is in existence. Some, although known for a century or more, are just beginning to find use. Some are very abundant, a few do not exist at all, except for a fleeting life as radioactive isotopes, byproducts of modern transmutation.

Copper, Silver, Gold

Group Ib

ELEMENT	ELECTRON SHELLS
$_{29}CU$	$= K_2L_8M_{18}N_1$
$_{47}Ag$	$= K_2L_8M_{18}N_{18}O_1$
$_{79}Au$	$= K_2L_8M_{18}N_{32}O_{18}P_1$

➤ OFTEN occurring uncombined at the surface of the earth, these "noble" metals were counted as treasures by man from earliest times. Our stock of them now in use probably includes some of the hoards of precious metals passed on from generation to generation through all recorded history.

Although these three coinage metals are soft, they are very durable. Their chemical inertness has led to their selection as a medium of exchange, which in turn has given them symbolic value far above that of other elements.

Georgius Agricola, authority on medieval mining methods and metallurgical processes, struggles with some of the moral problems connected with this symbolism, in his *De Re Metallica*. We quote from the 1912 translation by Herbert Clark Hoover and Lou Henry Hoover. (Although the idea that metals are evil may seem quaint, compare present-day arguments on the subject of atomic energy).

"Those who speak ill of the metals and refuse to make use of them, do not see that they accuse and condemn as wicked the Creator Himself, when they assert that He fashioned some things vainly and without good cause, and thus they regard Him as the Author of evils, which opinion is certainly not worthy of pious and sensible men. . . .

"Again, the products of the mines are not themselves the cause of war. Thus, for example, when a tyrant, inflamed with passion for a woman of great beauty, makes war on the inhabitants of her city, the fault lies in the unbridled lust of the tyrant and not in the beauty of the woman. Likewise, when another man, blinded by a passion for gold and silver, makes war upon a wealthy people, we ought not to blame the metals but transfer all blame to avarice. For frenzied deeds and disgraceful actions, which are wont to weaken and dishonor natural and civil laws, originate from our own vices. . . .

"When ingenious and clever men considered carefully the system of barter, which ignorant men of old employed and which even today is used by certain uncivilized and barbarous races, it appeared to them so troublesome and laborious that they invented money. Indeed, nothing more useful could have been devised, because a small amount of gold and silver is of as great value as things cumbrous and heavy; and so peoples far distant from one another can, by the use of money, trade very easily in those things which civilized life can scarcely do without."

Materials which are good in themselves must also be good for people, according to ancient reasoning. Therefore they used the precious metals as medicine. Modern experimental techniques show that, while many copper compounds are poisonous, organic compounds of silver and of gold have their places in medical therapy.

Alchemy

The value of gold led not only to war and to trade, but to attempts to make it artificially. This popular ancient and medieval pastime developed the extensive literature of alchemy, at once the pride and the shame of modern chemistry. Chemists take pride in the considerable progress their predecessors made in working with metals. They feel ashamed when they reflect that the alchemists were either extremely dishonest in trying to add weight and a yellow color to base metals and palm them off as gold, or extremely foolish to believe their own claims to be able to transmute the base metals into the genuine article.

The modern French chemist, Berthelot, became interested in a collection of ancient manuscripts containing alchemical recipes, and in 1887 published a study of them from the standpoint of the procedures they advise. Berthelot's explanation sheds more light on what the alchemists thought they were doing:

"Instead of coloring metals on the surface, to give them the appearance of gold or silver, Egyptian goldsmiths early learned to color them throughout, that is to say, to change them in nature. The processes employed by them consisted of making alloys of gold and of silver conserving the appearance of the metal. This is what they called *diplosis*, the art of 'doubling' the weight of gold and silver, an expression which was handed down to the alchemists along with the pretense of thus obtaining the metals, not simply mixed, but completely transformed. . . .

"In fact the word *diplosis* then implied sometimes simply increasing the weight of a precious metal by adding a metal of less value which did not change its appearance, sometimes making the piece of metal wholly gold or silver by transmuting the nature of the added metal. All metals are basically the same, according to the theories of the Platonists about primary matter. Even the silver of the transformation is a part of the original alloy, playing the role of ferment.

"All these procedures are as clear and positive, except for uncertainty about the meaning of some words, as our own recipes. It is all the more surprising, therefore, to see appear, in the midst of so precise a technical procedure, the chimera of true transmutation, correlated as it is with the intention of falsifying the metals. The falsifier, after repeatedly deceiving the public, must at length have ended by believing in the actuality of his work. He would come to believe, as much as his dupe, in that which he had at first proposed to do. Therefore the relationship of these recipes with those of the alchemists is thus, perhaps, completely established.

"I have already shown the identity of some recipes for gilding, in this papyrus, with the recipes for transmutation of Pseudo-Democritus . . . It is strikingly like the *diplosis* of Moses, a recipe as short and clear as that of the papyrus of Leiden and probably taken from the same sources, at least if we may judge by the role of Moses in this papyrus itself.

The procedure of Moses, explained in a few lines, is as follows:—

" 'Take some copper, some arsenic (orpiment), some sulfur and some lead; grind the mixture with oil of horseradish; roast it upon charcoal to desulfurize it; set it aside. Take 1 part of this roasted copper and 3 parts of gold; put it into a crucible; heat; and you will find all changed into gold, with the help of God.'

"This is an alloy of debased gold, analogous to those described above."

Modern Transmutation

The alchemist's dream of transmutation of the elements has at last come true, but in a very different way than he expected. Looking back now, we can see that the alchemist was trying to change the physical properties of the elements, and supposed that their nature would thus be changed.

The modern scientist changes the nature of the nucleus of an element, for example, by neutron bombardment, and the properties of the element, both physical and chemical, change accordingly.

One interesting modern application of transmutation turns the tables of the alchemists with almost poetic justice. This is the transmutation of gold into mercury 198 so that the wavelength of a green light band in its spectrum can be used as a standard for the measurement of length. This was established as an indestructible and exactly reproducible standard, precise to one part in 100 million, in 1948 by the U. S. National Bureau of Standards.

Photography

The action of light in darkening silver chloride was first reported by Carl Wilhelm Scheele in 1777. Shortly after 1800 several investigators recognized that the effect is due to the light at the blue end of the spectrum, and that silver bromide and silver iodide are also affected. Use of sodium hyposulfite to develop the image was discovered at about the same time, although the art of producing good pictures by photographic processes went through many stages. It took nearly a hundred years to get beyond the "wet plate" method, in which the photographer had to manufacture his plates as well as develop them, and to depend upon a sunny day for making his prints.

Electricity

Among the special uses for certain elements, none is more remarkable than the dependence of electrical industry upon copper. Its softness and ductility allow the metal to be drawn into wire which carries the electric current, and its electrical conductivity is greater than that of any other suitable metal except silver.

Alessandro Volta in 1800 wrote to Sir Joseph Banks, describing a piece of apparatus he had built: "The apparatus of which I speak to you, and which without doubt will surprise you, is only the assemblage of a number of good conductors of different sorts, arranged in a certain manner, 30, 40, 60 pieces, preferably, of copper, or better silver, each touching a piece of tin, or, which is better, of zinc, and an equal number of layers of water, or some other liquid which should be a better conductor than simple water like salt water, lye solution, etc., or pieces of cardboard, leather, etc., well soaked in these liquids; of which pads interposed between each couple or combination of the two different metals, alternating with each set, and always in the same order, of the three sorts of conductors; that is all there is to my new instrument."

Volta drew sparks from his battery, felt light shocks in the wrists of both hands when he touched the top and bottom plates with wet fingers, and admired the way it would, after each discharge, re-establish itself—"an inexhaustible charge, a perpetual effect." He did not notice the slight corrosion of the metal which accounts for the source of the electric current.

Corrosion occurs because slight differences in electric potential act like miniature batteries. By applying the principle of the electromotive series of metals, underground pipe or other metal installations can be protected. A metal forming an electromotive couple with the substance to be protected can be buried near it, for the purpose of being corroded. The valuable installation is thus protected instead of being consumed by small stray currents.

Silver's scarcity and beauty have kept it from being used for its electrical properties, except on one occasion. Allocation of copper for military use during World War II caused the designers of the atomic energy installations at Oak Ridge, Tenn., to use silver reserves of the government for electrical wiring there. Unlike the situation in a battery, no wear and tear on the metal is caused by passage of an electric current over a wire, and silver in an electric cable is safe.

Zinc, Cadmium, Mercury

Group IIb

ELEMENT   ELECTRON SHELLS
$_{30}Zn = K_2L_8M_{18}N_2$
$_{48}Cd = K_2L_8M_{18}N_{18}O_2$
$_{80}HG = K_2L_8M_{18}N_{32}O_{18}P_2$

→ MERCURY is the oldest of these three, in use in the arts, for it was one of the seven original metals, identified with the planet which bears the same name. The alchemists used it extensively, and considered mercury, sulfur and salt the three primeval materials out of which other substances are made. It is by no means certain, however, that they meant, by any of those three words, the substances we now call by those names.

Mercury is the only common metal which is liquid at ordinary temperatures. Its high surface tension makes it collect in almost spherical drops, so that it does not wet the surface of most materials. It combines, however, with gold and many other metals on contact. Its alloys are called amalgams.

The liquid property of mercury is utilized for several of the applications of this metal. In the mercury switch, contact is made when the liquid flows to one end of the tube containing it, and is broken when the tube is tilted the other way. Frozen mercury is used for casting metal parts, in a process similar to the "lost wax" process of bronze casting. At room temperature a mold is filled with liquid mercury. Chilled until the mercury becomes hard, the mold is removed, and a new mold is formed around the casting. When warmed to ordinary temperatures, the mercury can be poured out and the mold used for casting the part in a metal of higher melting point.

Mercury boilers operate on the principle of steam boilers.

Zinc was one of the first metals, in addition to the traditional seven, to be discovered, but it was not really appreciated until its role in protecting other metals from corrosion was recognized. This depends on its readiness to replace other metals in solution. The zinc tends to prevent corrosion of the other metal, while at the same time zinc itself does not rust in air. "Galvanized iron" has a coating of zinc.

Zinc is famous for the many organic compounds it forms. Similar cadmium compounds are unstable, sometimes explosive.

Cadmium is a recent discovery compared to its analogues. It is one of the metals which never occur uncombined but, once separated in metallic form, retains a bright, untarnished surface. The supply comes as a by-product of zinc smelting. The sulfide, Cd S, is a pigment supplied commercially as "cadmium yellow."

A new use for cadmium metal is in controls for atomic energy plants. One hundred pounds of cadmium is said to be needed for each 100,000 kilowatt output.

Zinc and Mercury

THE HERMETIC AND ALCHEMICAL WRITINGS *of Aureolus Philippus Theophratus Bombast, of Hohenheim, Called Paracelsus the Great. Now for the first time faithfully translated into English by Arthur Edward Waite, London, 1894 (Written about 1530 A.D.).*
Concerning Zinc:
➤THERE IS a certain metal, not commonly known, called zinc. It is of peculiar nature and origin. Many metals are adulterated in it. The metal itself is fluid, because it is generated from three fluid primals. It does not admit of hammering, only of fusion. Its colors are different from other colors, so that it resembles no other metals in the condition of growth. Such, I say, is this metal that its ultimate matter, to me at least, is not yet fully known. It does not admit of admixture; nor does it allow the fabrications of other metals. It stands by itself.
Concerning Quicksilver:
There is, moreover, a certain genus which is neither hammered nor founded, and it is a mineral water of metals. As water is to other substances, so is this with reference to metals. So far it should be a metal as Alchemy reduces it to malleability and capacity of being wrought. Commonly it has no consistence, but sometimes it has. The right opinion about it is that it is the primal matter of the Alchemists, who know how to get from it silver, gold, copper, etc., as the event proves. Possibly also tin, lead and iron can be made from it. Its nature is manifold and marvellous, and can only be studied with great toil and constant application. This, at all events, is clear, that it is the primal matter of the Alchemists in generating metals, and, moreover, a remarkable medicine. It is produced from Sulphur, Mercury and Salt, with this remarkable nature that it is a fluid but does not moisten, and runs about, though it has no feet. It is the heaviest of all the metals.

Concerning "Paracelsus"

➤IT IS EVIDENT from the quotation above that this early chemist was familiar with the two metals he describes, but a little confused about them as well. "Paracelsus" was a nickname he chose for himself, in order to claim that he was "better than Celsus." His name was Theophrastus Bombast.

His surname has given us the adjective "bombastic," which tells us what his contemporaries thought of this medieval physician. Yet, for all his oddities, he did good work in separating facts based on experiment from the fog of mysticism inherited from alchemy. He was especially interested in the use of chemical compounds in medicine.

By the time cadmium, middle member of this group, was discovered, chemistry was on surer ground.

Cadmium

NEW DETAILS RESPECTING CADMIUM. *By M. Stromeyer, in Annals of Philosophy, Vol. XIV, 1819.*

➔ M. STROMEYER has communicated to the Royal Society of Göttingen, at the meeting of Sept. 10, 1818, the first part of his researches on the new metal which he discovered in zinc and its oxides, and to which he has given the name of *cadmium*. Assisted by two of his pupils, M. Mahner, of Brunswick, and M. Siemens, of Hamburgh, he has not only verified his first results, but has been able to give a greater extent to his researches, and to reduce them to a great degree of precision. . . . He gives likewise the names of the different species of zinc, of its oxides, or of its ores, which contain cadmium. Among these last, M. Stromeyer has found it only in a very small proportion in some blends with the exception of some varieties of radiated blende of Przibram, in Hungary, which contains two or three percent of it. He likewise gives the process for procuring cadmium in a state of purity.

According to this process, we begin by dissolving in sulfuric acid the substances which contain cadmium, and through the solution, which must contain a sufficient excess of acid, a current of sulphuretted hydrogen gas must be passed. The precipitate formed is collected and well washed. It is then dissolved in concentrated muriatic acid, and the excess of acid driven off by evaporation. The residue is dissolved in water, and precipitated by carbonate of ammonia, of which an excess is added to redissolve the zinc and the copper that may have been precipitated by the sulphuretted hydrogen gas. The carbonate of cadmium, being well washed, is heated to drive off the carbonic acid, and the remaining oxide is reduced by mixing it with lamp-black, and exposing it to a moderate red heat in a glass, or earthen retort.

The color of cadmium is a fine white, with a slight shade of bluish-grey, and approaching much to that of tin. Like this last metal, it has a strong luster, and takes a good polish. Its texture is perfectly compact, and its fracture hackly. It crystallizes easily in octahedrons, and presents at its surface on cooling the appearance of leaves of fern. It is soft, very flexible, and yields readily to the file, or the knife. It stains pretty strongly; however, it is harder than tin, and surpasses it in tenacity. It is likewise very ductile, and may be reduced to fine wires, or thin plates; yet, when long hammered, it scales off in different places.

Its specific gravity, without being hammered, is 8.5040, at the temperature of 62°; when hammered, it is 8.6944. It melts before being heated to redness, and is volatilized at a heat not much greater than what is necessary to volatilize mercury. Its vapor has no peculiar odor. It condenses in drops as readily as mercury, which, on congealing, present distinct traces of crystallization.

Cadmium is as little altered by exposure to the air as tin. When heated in the open air, it burns as readily as this last metal, and is converted into a brownish-yellow oxide, which appears usually under the form of a smoke of the same color; but which is very fixed.

Nitric acid dissolves it easily cold; diluted sulfuric acid, muriatic acid, and even acetic acid, attack it with disengagement of hydrogen gas; but their action is very feeble, especially that of acetic acid, even when it is assisted by heat. The solutions are colorless, and are not precipitated by water.

Titanium, Zirconium, Hafnium

Group IVα

ELEMENT	ELECTRON SHELLS
$_{22}Ti$	$= K_2L_8M_{10}N_2$
$_{40}Zr$	$= K_2L_8M_{18}N_{10}O_2$
$_{72}Hf$	$= K_2L_8M_{18}N_{32}O_{10}P_2$

Excerpts from the following:
ANALYTICAL ESSAYS *towards promoting the chemical knowledge of mineral substances, by Martin Henry Klaproth. Translated from the German, London, 1801.*

Titanium

→ THE DISCOVERY of Titanium, in the red Hungarian shörl, and in the small hair-brown crystals, from the country about Passau, having so much excited the attention of chemists and mineralogists, it was natural to expect, that this new metallic substance would also be found in other places. The event has shewn, that this expectation was not ill founded. . . .

Within a few years a fossil has been brought into notice by the name of *Menachanite,* which has been found in the parish of Menachan, in Cornwall, and consists of grey-black, sand-like grains, obeying the magnet. Mr. McGregor, of Menachan, who dedicates his study to mineralogical chemistry, has given not only the first information of this fossil, but also a full narrative of his chemical researches concerning it. The chief result of these is, that Menachanite has for its constituent parts iron, and a peculiar *metallic oxyd of an unknown nature.*

By the following examination it will appear, that this substance, which, besides iron, forms the second chief component principle of Menachanite, is precisely the very same which constitutes the Hungarian red shörl; namely *oxyd of titanium.* With this opinion also, most of the phenomena, noted down by McGregor, in his operation with Menachanite agree.

Though I was easily convinced of this fact by my own experiments, it seemed, on the other hand, very difficult to separate entirely the iron from the titanic oxyd; and, hence, to ascertain the true proportion of these two ingredients to each other. . . .

Chemical Examination of the supposed Hungarian Red Shörl.

The sum of these results furnishes several arguments, upon the strength of which I do not scruple to consider the *red shörl,* as it has been hitherto called, of *Boinik* in *Hungary,* as a natural metallic oxyd. The phenomena, upon which I ground my conclusion, are:

That the white earth, subjected to ignition, becomes yellow, reddish, and, in contact with charcoal, blueish; that it produces a yellow enamel color; that it is precipitated from its solutions in acids, by Prussian alkali, gallic acid [tincture of galls], and alkaline sulphuret; that, when treated in the humid way with tin and zinc, it is recovered in dark flakes, the solution then acquiring a red and blue color; and, lastly, that it shews a very strong tendency to combine with oxygen. It is on account of this last property that the crude fossil, as being fully saturated with that acidifying principle, is insoluble in acids, and is rendered capable of solution only when, by ignition with an alkali, it is deprived of a part of its oxygen. For this reason, likewise, when I ignited the rough fossil, in a subsequent analytical experiment, with only two parts of vegetable alkali, the earth obtained did not prove so white and loose as that fused with five or six parts. It also dissolved but imperfectly, in muriatic acid, and not at all in the sulfuric and nitric.

To these facts must be added the phenomenon, that the muriatic solution of that substance became changed into a blue tincture by zinc; but when decanted, and exposed to open air, in a warm place, it again lost its color, by imbibing oxygen, and deposited a white earth.

It is sufficiently shewn, by several of its properties, that this metallic substance does not belong to any of those at present known, but rather deserves to be reputed a new, peculiar genus of metals. Among these, the copious *brown-red precipitate*, produced by the gallic acid [tincture of galls], furnishes an easy test and specific means of distinguishing it from other metals.

Zirconium
On the Jargon of Ceylon

→ THE OBSTINACY with which the jargon resisted every attempt to decompose it . . . abated my ardour in pursuing farther this experiment. . . .

I saturated the whole of the sulfuric solution with crystallized alkali, prepared from tartar; on which the earth, which separated, imparted to the mixture an uniform, milky appearance. The earth thus deposited and washed, was subjected, while yet moist, to the following experiments.

In diluted and gently warmed sulfuric acid it dissolved without any effervescence, though it had been precipitated by carbonated alkali. . . . I continued adding this earth to the acid, until the last portion gave the solution an opaline appearance; but this again disappeared on the addition of a slight quantity of sulfuric acid, so that the solution then became clear. After cooling, it congealed into a milk-white, pulpy substance. For this reason I again added a little sulfuric acid, which, assisted by a low heat, rendered the solution again limpid, so that it no longer coagulated in the cold. I then left it standing at rest in a low temperature, and after some days I found the greatest part of it shot into small, detached, and clear crystalline groups, in radii of a flattened quadrilateral columnar form, diverging from a common center, and terminating in sharp points. Their taste was but little sour, and left on the tongue a slight astringency. When thrown into water, they soon and easily dissolved, at the same time that they lost their limpidity and became turbid. The remainder of the solution still afforded some crystals of a fine granular form; and the last portion thickened into an irregularly shaped mass.

It is, then, manifest from the foregoing experiments that the *Jargonia*, or jargonic earth, is entirely different from the aluminous. That it is equally distinct from the magnesian earth has already been proved by the total absence of all magnesian taste in the sulfuric solution, as well as by its incapability of absorbing carbonic acid. However, that no circumstance might be left unexplored in this examination, I re-dissolved in sulfuric acid the portion that yet remained; and having saturated with carbonate of lime the solution heated to boiling, I filtered the fluid from it after cooling. But neither the taste, nor any other reagents, could discover the smallest sign of magnesia.

Hafnium

On the Missing Element of Atomic Number 72. Letter from Universitets Institut for teoretisk Fysik, Copenhagen, January 2, by D. Coster and G. Hevesy. In Nature, London, *January 20, 1923.*

→ SINCE Moseley's discovery of the fundamental laws of the X-ray emission, it has become quite clear that the most simple and conclusive characteristic of a chemical element is given by its X-ray spectrum. In addition, Moseley's laws allow us to calculate very accurately the wave-lengths of the X-ray spectral lines for any element in the periodic table, if those of the elements in its neighborhood are known. Taking into account that the presence of a very small proportion of a definite element in any chemical substance suffices to give a good X-ray spectrum of this element, it is quite evident that for the eventual discovery of any unknown element X-ray spectroscopy, especially as it has been developed by Siegbahn, represents the most effective method.

In the *Comptes rendus* of the Paris Academy of Sciences for May 22, 1922, Dauvillier announced the detection by means of X-ray spectroscopy of the element 72 in a mixture of rare-earth metals. This element was identified by Urbain with a rare-earth element, which he called celtium, the presence of which he had previously suspected in the same sample. For different reasons, however, we think that Dauvillier's and Urbain's conclusions are not justified. It appears from Dauvillier's paper that at any rate the quantity of the element 72 in the sample, if present, must have been so small that it seems very improbable that the element 72 should be identical with the element which in former papers Urbain claims to have detected in the same sample by investigation of the optical spectrum and of the magnetic properties. The only lines which Dauvillier claims to have detected are the lines L α 1 and L β 2, both of which he finds to be extremely faint (*extrêmement faible*). The wave-lengths he gives, however, for these lines are about 4 X.u. (1 X.u. $= 10^{-11}$ cm.) smaller than those which are obtained by a rational interpolation in the wave-length tables of Hjalmar and Coster, for the elements in the neighborhood of 72.

From a theoretical point of view it appears very doubtful that the element 72 should be a rare earth. It was announced in 1895 by Julius Thomsen from Copenhagen that from general consideration of the laws of the periodic system we must expect between tantalum, which in many compounds possesses five valencies, and the trivalent rare-earths, a tetravalent element homologous to zirconium. The same view has also recently been put forward by Bury on the basis of chemical considerations, and by Bohr on the basis of his theory of atomic structure. It is one of the most striking results of the latter theory, that a rational interpretation of the appearance of the rare-earth metals in the periodic system could be given. For these elements, according to Bohr, we witness the gradual development of the group of 4-quantum electrons from a group containing 18 electrons into a group of 32 electrons, the numbers of electrons in the groups of 5- and 6-quantum electrons remained unchanged. Bohr was able to conclude that in the element lutecium (71) the group of 4-quantum electrons is complete, and we consequently must expect that in the neutral atom of the next element (72) the number of electrons moving in 5- and 6-quantum orbits must exceed that in the rare-earths by one. The element 72 can therefore not be a rare-earth but must be an homologue of zirconium.

In view of the great theoretical importance of the question we have tried to settle it by an experimental investigation of the X-ray spectrum of extractions of zirconium minerals. We have succeeded in detecting six lines which must be ascribed to the element 72 (in Siegbahn's notation Lα 1, α 2, β 1, β 2, β 3, and γ 1. The complication was met that the line L α 1 and α 2 lie almost exactly in the place corresponding in the spectrum to the zirconium K α 1, and α 2, lines of the second order. Difficulties which might arise from this fact may easily be avoided by keeping the tension on the tube between the critical tension of the zirconium K-lines (18,000 volts) and that of the L-lines of the missing element (10,000 volts). Besides, the relative intensity of the K α lines is so different from that of the two L α lines that any ambiguity is already thereby excluded. Not only the L α lines but also the lines Lβ 1, β 2, and β 3 were, as regards their mutual distance and their relative intensity, in exact agreement with the expectation. The values which we obtained for the wave-lengths of the six mentioned lines all agree within one X.u. with those found by interpolation. Between our values for the lines L α 1 and L β 2, and those published by Dauvillier, however, there exists the discrepancy referred to of about 4 X.u. (in general for other elements which have been measured by Dauvillier and by Coster the discrepancy is never more than 2 X.u.). Exposures under different conditions as well as a thorough discussion of the plates showed that the new lines found during our investigation cannot be ascribed to the first or higher order spectrum of any other known element. Our provisional results are, Lα 1 = 1565.5; α 2 = 1576; β 1 = 1371.4; β 2 = 1323.7; β 3 = 1350.2; γ 1 = 1177 X.u. More accurate and complete data as well as photographs of the spectrum will soon be published.

In a Norwegian zirconium mineral the new lines were so intense that we estimate the quantity of the element 72 present in it to be at least equal to one per cent. Besides we investigated with low tension on the tube a sample of "pure zirconium oxide." Also with this specimen the L α lines were found, but very faint. It seems to be very probable that ordinary zirconium contains at least from 0.01 to 0.1 per cent of the new element. Especially the latter circumstance proves that the element 72 is chemically homologous to zirconium. Experiments are in progress to isolate the new element and to determine its chemical properties.

For the new element we propose the ñame *Hafnium* (Hafniae = Copenhagen).

Vanadium, Niobium or Columbium, Tantalum

Group Va

ELEMENT	ELECTRON SHELLS
$_{23}V$	$= K_2L_8M_{11}N_2$
$_{41}Nb$	$= K_2L_8M_{18}N_{12}O_1$
$_{73}Ta$	$= K_2L_8M_{18}N_{32}O_{11}P_2$

Vanadium

Extracts from UEBER DAS VANADIN . . . (*On Vanadin, a new Metal, found in bar iron from Eckersholm, an iron foundry which gets its ore from Taberg in Smoland*). *By N. G. Sefström. From Kongl. Vetensk Acad. Handl. f. 1830. Published in Annalen der Physik und Chemie (Poggendorff), Vol. 22, Leipzig, 1831.*

→ MANY YEARS ago the Bergmeister Rinmann devised a method for easily detecting whether an iron were cold-short, which depends upon the circumstance that such an iron upon etching with hydrochloric acid gives a black powder. On one occasion, when I needed an iron which was not cold-short, and for the purpose investigated iron from Eckersholm by this method, which I have described in the Annalen des Eisencomtoirs for 1825, S. 155, it gave, to my astonishment, the reaction for cold-shortness, although the iron from Taberg is considered the softest and toughest that we have.

Time did not then allow me to clear up this behavior; but in April, 1830, I took up the investigation again, in order to see whether the black powder contained phosphorus, or consisted of some other material which it was important for me to know. Accordingly I dissolved a considerable amount of this iron in hydrochloric acid and examined the remaining black powder. During the solution the circumstance appeared that part of the iron, especially that setting free the black powder, dissolved faster than the rest, so that in the middle of the iron bar hollow veins were left.

Upon analysis of the black powder there were found in it silica, iron, alumina, calcium, copper, cobalt, and a substance which in certain respects resembled chromium and in others uranium. In what combinations these substances occurred could not be determined, since the small amount of black powder did not exceed 2 decigrams, and of this more than half was composed of silicic acid.

After several tests it was discovered that it was not chromium, and the following comparisons show also that it is equally unlikely that it is uranium. In this it is to be noted that the highest oxidation products were compared with one another, that, however, Vanadin resembles tellurium in its lower oxidation forms.

Reactions of Uranium Oxide   Reactions of Vanadin

Solution in Hydrochloric Acid

Reactions of Uranium Oxide	Reactions of Vanadin
Color: pure yellow	Color: orange yellow
Behavior with Ammonium Hydroxide	
Gives a yellow precipitate, especially upon warming	Gave no precipitate and with excess of ammonia the solution upon warming became colorless
With Ammonium Carbonate in Excess	
Is precipitated on heating	Is not precipitated
With Potassium Ferrocyanide	
Gives a brown precipitate	Gave a green precipitate
Before the Blowpipe:	
With large admixture of Borax	
The yellow glass becomes colorless, but not the green	The green glass may become colorless, but not the yellow
With Soda in the Oxidizing Flame	
Does not dissolve in it	Is easily dissolved in it

These reactions were later confirmed in the month of May in the laboratory of Prof. Berzelius. The metal was reduced by roasting in hydrogen gas, and it was thus discovered that it possesses a lower oxidation compound, giving with acids a blue-green solution, and that this as well as the higher oxide is soluble in alkalies.

A complete analysis could not be made at that time on account of other matters; and the small supply, amounting to less than 2 centigrams, was used up.

In the autumn the research was again taken up and then carried on in the laboratory of Prof. Berzelius. There the new metal was first isolated from the iron bars; but the yield even from several pounds of dissolved iron amounted to so little, that I procured a quantity of slag from the iron, from which I got a sufficient amount for investigation. . . .

Name of the new metal—since this makes no difference to it, I have derived it from *Vanadis*, an alternate name of Freya, the most important goddess in Scandinavian mythology.

Columbium

Extracts from AN ANALYSIS OF A MINERAL SUBSTANCE FROM NORTH AMERICA, *Containing a Metal Hitherto Unknown. By Charles Hatchett. Philosophical Transactions of the Royal Society of London, 1802. Read Nov. 26, 1801.*

➤ IN THE COURSE of the last summer, when I was examining and arranging some minerals in the British Museum, I observed a small specimen of a dark-colored heavy substance, which attracted my attention, on account of some resemblance which it had with the Siberian chromate of iron, on which at that time I was making experiments.

Upon referring to Sir Hans Sloane's catalogue, I found that this specimen was only described as "a very heavy black stone, with golden streaks," which proved to be yellow mica; and it appeared, that it had been sent, with various specimens of iron ores, to Sir Hans Sloane, by Mr. Winthrop, of Massachusetts.

The name of the mine, or place where it was found, is also noted in the catalogue; the writing however is scarcely legible: it appears to be an Indian name, (Nautneauge); but I am informed by several American gentlemen, that many of the Indian names (by which certain small districts, hills, &c. were forty or fifty years ago distinguished) are now totally forgotten, and European names have been adopted in the room of them. This may have been the case in the present instance; but, as the other specimens sent by Mr. Winthrop were from the mines of Massachusetts, there is every reason to believe that the mineral substance in question came from one of them, although it may not now be easy to identify the particular mine. . . .

The external color is dark brownish gray.

The internal color is the same, inclining to iron gray.

The longtiudinal fracture is imperfectly lamellated; and the cross fracture shows a fine grain.

The luster is vitreous, slightly inclining in some parts to metallic luster.

It is moderately hard, and is very brittle.

The color of the streak or powder is dark chocolate brown.

The particles are not attracted by the magnet.

The specific gravity, at temp. 65°, is 5.918. . . .

The preceding experiments show that the ore which has been analyzed consists of iron combined with an unknown substance, and that the latter constitutes more than three-fourths of the whole. This substance is proved to be of a metallic nature, by the colored precipitates which it forms with prussiate of potash, and with tincture of galls; by the effects which zinc produces, when immersed in the acid solutions; and by the color which it communicates to phosphate of ammonia, or rather to concrete phosphoric acid, when melted with it.

Moreover, from the experiments made with the blowpipe, it seems to be one of those metallic substances which retain oxygen with great obstinacy, and are therefore of difficult reduction.

It is an acidifiable metal; for the oxide reddens litmus paper, expels carbonic acid, and forms combinations with the fixed alkalis. But it is very different from the acidifiable metals which have of late been discovered; for,

1. It remains white when digested with nitric acid.

2. It is soluble in the surfuric and muriatic acids, and forms colorless solutions, from which it may be precipitated, in the state of a white flocculent oxide, by zinc, by the fixed alkalis, and by ammonia. Water also precipitates it from the sulfuric solution, in the state of a sulfate.

3. Prussiate of potash produces a copious and beautiful olive-green precipitate.

4. Tincture of galls forms orange or deep yellow precipitates.

5. Unlike other metallic acids, it refuses to unite with ammonia.

6. When mixed and distilled with sulfur, it does not combine with it so as to form a metallic sulfuret.

7. It does not tinge any of the fluxes, except phosphoric acid, with which, even in the humid way, it appears to have a very great affinity.

8. When combined with potash and dissolved in water, it forms precipitates, upon being added to solutions of tungstate of potash, molybdate of potash, cobaltate of ammonia, and the alkaline solution of iron.

These properties completely distinguish it from the other acidifiable metals, *viz.* arsenic, tungsten, molybdenum, and chromium; as to the other metals lately discovered, such as uranium, titanium, and tellurium, they are still farther removed from it. . . .

I am much inclined to believe, that the time is perhaps not very distant, when some of the newly-discovered metals, and other substances, which are now considered as simple, primitive, and distinct bodies, will be found to be compounds. Yet I only entertain this opinion as a probability; for, until an advanced state of chemical knowledge shall enable us to compose, or at least to decompose, these bodies, each must be classed and denominated as a substance *sui generis.* Considering therefore, that the metal which has been examined is so very different from those hitherto discovered, it appeared that it should be distinguished by a peculiar name; and, having consulted with several of the eminent and ingenious chemists of this country, I have been induced to give it the name of Columbium.

Columbite remains as the name of the ore, and columbium as the alternate name of the metal. The ore seems to have been sent to England by John Winthrop who was the grandson of John Winthrop the Younger, first Governor of Connecticut. The specimen which Hatchett analyzed came from New London, Conn., according to tradition in the Winthrop family, or from Middletown, according to the opinion of the Connecticut Geological Survey. Remarkable deposits of the ore are found in a Middletown quarry, their report states.

The element was re-discovered in Europe so closely associated with tantalum that the properties of the two elements were not completely distinguished for many years. The European name of Niobium, now declared official, is for the daughter of Tantalus. European chemists followed Berzelius in prejudice against place names for elements, and in favor of names drawn from ancient mythology.

Tantalum

Extract from a MEMOIR *on the Properties of Yttria Earth Compared with those of Glucine; on the Fossils in which the Former of these Earths is Contained; and on the Discovery of a new Substance of a Metallic Nature. By A. G. Ekeberg. Phil. Mag., Vol. XIV, London, 1802.*

→ THOUGH the mineral substance I discovered [says Ekeberg] contains yttria, it could not be classed in a system of mineralogy as a species of earth, on account of the more abundant mixture it contains of another equally remarkable, and which must increase the class of metals, already very numerous. I found this substance in two fossils, obtained from different places; in one of them, it was united with iron and manganese; and in the other, with the former of these metals and gadoline.

This new metallic substance is distinguished by its insolubility in all acids. The only reagent which has any action on it is caustic fixed alkali. When subjected to heat with this alkali, if the mass be then lixiviated, it partly dissolves in the water, and suffers itself to be precipitated from that solution, by means of an acid—but without the precipitate being in any manner attacked, whatever be the quantity of the acid employed. When separated by the filter, and dried, it remains under the form of an exceedingly fine white powder, which does not change its color even at a red heat. If the remaining mass be treated with acids, the same powder is obtained. Its specific gravity, after being brought to red heat, is 6.500. It is fusible by the blowpipe, by the addition of alkaline phosphate and borate of soda, but communicates no color to the flux.

Exposed to a strong heat in a crucible, without any other mixture than pounded charcoal, it is reduced to a button moderately hard, having some metallic splendor at its surface, but a dull blackish fracture. Acids have no other action on this kind of regulus, but that of bringing it to the state of white oxide in which it was before. The circumstances of the reduction as well as the specific gravity of this singular substance, seem to assign it a place among the metals, and I have sufficient reasons for being persuaded that it is none of those already known. The substances with which it might be confounded are the oxides of tin, tungsten, and titanium, which are soluble in caustic alkalies, and which, under some circumstances, resist acids. But the oxide of tin is easily dissolved and reduced; tungsten immediately discovers itself by its solubility in ammonia, and by the blue color which it communicates to phosphate of soda: the oxide of titanium gives a hyacinth color to borax, and becomes soluble in acids by fusion with carbonate of potash. . . .

Taking advantage of the usage which admits mythologic appelations, and to express the property which the new metal has, of not becoming saturated with the acids in which it is immersed, I shall apply to it the name of *Tantalus*.

Chromium, Molybdenum, Tungsten

Group VIα

ELEMENT	ELECTRON SHELLS
$_{24}Cr$	$= K_2 L_8 M_{13} N_1$
$_{42}Mo$	$= K_2 L_8 M_{18} N_{13} O_1$
$_{74}W$	$= K_2 L_8 M_{18} N_{32} O_{12} P_2$

Chromium

ANALYSIS OF THE RED LEAD OF SIBERIA; *with Experiments on the new Metal it contains. By Citizen Vauquelin. In Nicholson's Journal of Natural Philosophy, Chemistry and the Arts, Vol. II, London, 1798.*

➤ WHEN an unknown substance is to be examined, the only method to ascertain whether it has been better described, is to examine its properties, and compare them with those of other bodies; an operation which supposes a knowledge of all that has been before described in natural history. And when, after an accurate comparison of the properties of the body under examination with those of other bodies, it is found that none of these last exhibit the whole of those properties, a fair conclusion may be formed that the body is unknown, and consequently that it is new.

After this point is determined, it becomes necessary, in order to make it known to others, that its distinctive characters should be clearly ascertained, and a name given to it, for the purpose of brief designation, and of inscription in the catalogue of human knowledge. . . .

From these considerations I have thought fit to adopt the name *chrome*, which was proposed to me by Cit. Haüy, to designate the new metal found in the native red lead. In truth, this name does not perfectly agree with the complete metal, because it has no very distinct color; and because, even if it had one, this would not be a sufficient reason, since every metal has a more or less peculiar color.

But it agrees wonderfully well with its combinations with oxygen, which afford a green oxide, or a red acid, according to the proportions of that principle, and because each of its primary combinations communicates its color to all the secondary combinations into which it enters; properties which belong to it almost exclusively.

Scheele on Mo and W

THE COLLECTED PAPERS OF CARL WILHELM SCHEELE, *Translated from the Swedish and German Originals by Leonard Dobbin. London: G. Bell & Sons, Ltd., 1931.*

Molybdenum

Experiments with Lead-Ore: Molybdaena. Kongl. Vetenskaps Academiens Handlingar, 39, (1778).

→ I DO NOT mean the ordinary lead-ore that is met with in apothecaries' shops, for this is very different from that concerning which I now wish to communicate my experiments to the Royal Academy. I mean here that which in Cronstedt's Mineralogy is called *Molybdaena membranacea nitens,* and with which Quist and others probably made their experiments. The kinds I had occasion to submit to tests were got in different places but they were all found to be of the same nature and composed of the same constituents. . . .

Earth of molybdaena is of an acid nature. Its solution reddens litmus; soap solution becomes white, and liver of sulfur is precipitated. (*b*) The solution has also some action on metals. When it is boiled with filings of all base metals, the solution at last becomes bluish. (*c*) If very little alkali of tartar [potassium carbonate] is added, the earth is dissolved in greater quantity in water, and after cooling crystallises in small confused crystals. This small quantity of alkali brings it about that the earth is not volatilized in the open fire. (*d*) The solution, while it is still hot, shows its acid property more strongly. It reddens litmus more; it effervesces with chalk,

white magnesia, and earth of alum, whence intermediate salts
arise which are very difficultly dissolved in water. (*e*) It precipitates silver, quick-silver, and lead dissolved in acid of nitre;
also lead dissolved in acid of salt. These precipitates are reduced upon charcoal, when the melted earth sinks into the
charcoal. The other metals are not precipitated, neither is
corrosive mercury. (*f*) The earth of heavy spar, dissolved
in acid of salt or of nitre, is likewise precipitated. This precipitate is not regenerated heavy spar [barium sulfate], because it is dissolved by cold water, a property which does not
belong to regenerated heavy spar. The solutions of other
kinds of earth are not precipitated. (*g*) The solution also
drives out the aerial acid from fixed and volatile alkalies; with
these it yields neutral salts which precipitate all metallic solutions. Gold, corrosive sublimate, zinc, and manganese are
precipitated white; iron and tin in acid of salt, brown; cobalt,
rose-red; copper, blue; alum and lime solutions, white. If the
sal ammoniac composed of the volatile alkali and the earth
of molybdaena is distilled, the earth parts with its volatile
alkali at a moderate heat and remains in the retort as a grey
powder.

Tungsten

*The Constituents of Tungsten. Kongl. Vetenskaps Academ-
iens Nya Handlinger. 2 (1781).*
→ THE CONSTITUENTS of this variety of stone seem probably
to be still unknown to chemists. Cronstedt enumerates it
amongst the ferruginous varieties of stone, under the name
of *Ferrum calciforme, terra quadam incognita intime mixtum.*
That which I used for my experiments is pearl coloured and
taken from the iron mine of Bitsberg: and as I made many
experiments upon it and have ascertained its constituents, I
take the liberty of presenting the following to the Royal
Academy:
1. (*a*) In the fire, tungsten does not undergo any perceptible change, neither has glass of borax any special action upon
it; (*b*) but microcosmic salt gives with it, before the blowpipe, a seagreen coloured glass. When such a glass bead is
kept in fusion before the outermost tip of a candle flame the
colour gradually disappears; a very little nitre also takes away
the colour instantly, but it appears again when the blue candle
flame is driven upon it. . . .
When acid tungsten is calcined in a crucible, it loses its
property of being dissolved afterwards by water. That the acid
is inclined to attract phlogiston is seen from the blue colour
which it shows in fluxes. . . . Solution of liver of sulfur was
precipitated green by our acid, but phlogisticated alkali, white.
This latter precipitate is soluble in water. When some drops
of acid of salt are mixed with the solution of this acid in water,
and spread upon polished iron, zinc, or even tin, or when

these metals are placed in the acid, the acid acquires a fine blue colour.

Since the acid of molybdaena also assumes a blue colour from the last-named metals, it is easy to suppose that the acid of tungsten is nothing else than acid of molybdaena. But since in other experiments it behaves quite differently, our acid must also be of a different nature; because (1) the acid of molybdaena is volatile and melts in the fire, which does not occur with acid of tungsten. (2) The first-named acid has a stronger affinity for phlogiston, which is seen from its union with sulfur, and the change it undergoes on calcination with oil. (3) *Calx molybdaenata* does not become yellow with acid of nitre and is dissolved by it quite easily. With tungsten the contrary occurs. (4) *Terra ponderosa molybdaenata* is soluble in water, but not the same variety of earth united with our acid; and (5) acid of molybdaena has a weaker attraction for lime than our acid, because when *calx molybdaenata* is digested with a solution of the previously mentioned sal ammoniac tungsten is again obtained. The iron which is obtained from some sorts of tungsten ought to be regarded as accidentally pertaining to it.

Manganese, Technetium, Rhenium

Group VIIα

ELEMENT   ELECTRON SHELLS
$$_{25}Mn = K_2L_8M_{13}N_2$$
$$_{43}Tc = K_2L_8M_{18}N_{14}O_1$$
$$_{75}Re = K_2L_8M_{18}N_{32}O_{13}P_2$$

The analogues of manganese were among the mysteriously missing elements until very recently. The stories of their discoveries are told here. Manganese itself was confused with magnesium when it was first described, because the elements were both found in the same locality. Scheele straightened out the properties due to maganese, and discovered chlorine in the process.

Manganese

COLLECTED PAPERS *of Carl Wilhelm Scheele, translated by Dobbin,* London, 1931. Date of original publication, 1774.
➔ THE VARIETIES of manganese have attracted the attention of chemists for many years past. Yet the investigations have

attained little more than to discover those properties which might serve to distinguish them from other kinds of stones; at least it is not generally known that anything further has been done with them besides the dissertation of the year 1767, in which Westfield undertook to demonstrate their constituents. Nevertheless my experiments will plainly show that he has been too hasty in this. It is unnecessary to enumerate the many varieties of manganese that I examined, because they all agree in their chief properties.

A clear colorless glass flux always becomes more or less red from manganese, entirely according to quantity; and if the flux is a little alkaline, the color inclines to violet. It is known that arsenic, gypsum, and calx of tin destroy the red color in such a glass and render it clear and colorless. So far as the arsenic is concerned, the reason is evident from its constituents; for in this case the phlogiston of the arsenic unites with the manganese dissolved in the red glass, and takes away the color, and the acid of arsenic unites with the alkali of the glass. In this connection it is observed that the experiment succeeds even in a covered crucible, which would in no case go on with gypsum and calx of tin; but when charcoal powder is added to it, an effervescence arises, the red color disappears, and the glass becomes clear and colorless. . . .

When a solution of manganese is diluted with much water, and is afterwards precipitated by caustic alkali, the precipitate comes down brown at the very beginning, and behaves like pure manganese. It is clearly seen here that the air in the water is sufficient to take up the inflammable principle in the manganese as soon as it is separated from its acid. For the same reason, the manganese precipitated from its solution by lime water, likewise falls down brown, but when more of a concentrated solution of manganese is mixed with it, and it is afterwards precipitated with caustic alkali, a white precipitate is obtained. . . .

When an ounce and a half of phlogisticated manganese was distilled in a glass retort over a strong fire, a large quantity of aerial acid went over, together with some drops of water. While the retort was still warm, the manganese was poured out upon paper, whereupon it immediately became red-hot and kindled the paper.

Rhenium

Two New Elements of the Manganese Group. Nature, July 11, 1925.

➤ THE RECENT discovery of the two missing elements of the manganese group by Dr. Noddack and Fräulein Tacke of Berlin is of interest not only as an important step toward the completion of the periodic table but also on account of the method used in the research. . . .

In the first place, it was necessary to find some material in which the new elements might reasonably be expected to occur. A study of the neighboring elements suggested two possible sources; the first that of the platinum ores, the second a mineral such as columbite.

The platinum ores contain the elements chromium to copper, ruthenium to silver, osmium to gold, or, expressed in atomic numbers, 24 to 29, 44 to 47, and 76 to 79. Columbite, on the other hand, contains, among many other elements those of atomic number 39 to 42 and 71 to 74. Here, therefore, were two minerals in either of which the missing elements 43 and 75 might well be found.

In endeavoring to form an estimate of the amounts of the elements 43 and 75 which might be present in these minerals, the authors employed an ingenious argument. The constitution of the earth's crust is now fairly well known, and it is possible to assign to the various elements numbers indicating the frequency of their occurrence. A study of these figures indicates that elements of odd atomic number are less common than those of even atomic number; in fact, an odd element is ten or twenty times less abundant than the succeeding even element.

As ruthenium (44) and osmium (76) constitute about $2x10^{-12}$ and $2x10^{-11}$ of the earth's crust, it was deduced that the elements 43 and 75 would form about 10^{-13} and 10^{-12} of the earth's outer layer. As the frequency of occurrence of platinum is 10^{-9}, the amount of the elements 43 and 75 in the platinum ores should be from 10^{-5} to 10^{-4}, and as niobium, one of the chief constituents of columbite, forms 10^{-7} of the earth's surface, columbite was estimated to contain from 10^{-5} to 10^{-6} of the missing elements. In this way Drs. Noddack and Tacke obtained some idea of the extent to which the chemical processes of extraction would have to be carried if measurable quantities of the new substances were to be obtained.

It was a fairly straightforward matter to predict some of the chemical properties of the new elements from a consideration of their neighbors in the periodic table. Thus it appeared probable that both would form oxides X_2O_7, and that these oxides would readily sublime on account of the small difference of temperature between their melting- and boiling-points. Again, for example, it was argued that the eka-manganeses would resemble chromium in so far as no sulfides would be formed from aqueous solutions. These and other chemical properties were used in the chemical treatment of the ores.

Attention was first directed to the platinum ores as offering the highest chance of success. After preliminary chemical treatment, the residue of 80 gm. of a Russian ore was strongly heated alternately in oxygen and hydrogen. Among the deposits on the walls of the vessel was found a very small quantity of white microscopic needle crystals. These needles became dark in color when treated with a stream of hydrogen sulfide, while a subsequent heating in oxygen resulted in the reappearance of the white sublimation product on the colder part of the vessel. An aqueous solution of these crystals gave no precipitate either with hydrogen sulfide or ammonium sulfide. As such behavior was to be expected from the elements 43 and 75 and from none of the other known elements in the solution, it was presumed that this substance contained the missing elements. Further attempts at concentration resulted in a loss of the material. . . .

[Similar material obtained from the columbite ore was subjected to X-ray analysis, and certain lines identified as belonging to it.]

As a result of this careful research work, the existence on the earth of the elements of atomic number 43 and 75 appears to be definitely established, a fact which is all the more interesting because certain writers have put forward arguments suggesting that a search for the eka-manganeses must prove fruitless. . . .

The authors suggest that the two newly discovered elements should be named Masurium (Ma) and Rhenium (Re) after the district of Eastern Prussia and after the Rhine respectively. Whether these names will meet with such widespread approval as the research itself remains to be seen.

Production of "the ekamanganeses" in the atomic pile has now proved a sure way to test the properties of these elements. Rhenium has proved to be the whole of the material. Drs. Noddack and Tacke isolated from their minerals. No. 43 has been prepared by transmutation but seems to be one of the elements which does not exist on earth, under present conditions.

Technetium

SOME CHEMICAL PROPERTIES OF ELEMENT 43—*Part II. By C. Perrier and E. Segrè. Journal of Chemical Physics, Vol. 7, 1939.*

WE HAVE found a very simple method for extracting the activity, i.e., the element 43, from the bombarded molybdenum. Since the activity is confined to a very thin layer, determined by the range of the deuterons in the molybdenum target, it is sufficient to attack only the surface of the molybdenum in order to carry the activity into solution. The simplest way for doing this is to boil the molybdenum in ammonium hydroxide after addition of a small amount of hydrogen peroxide. In some hours it is possible to extract in this way a large fraction of the active material mixed with only a few milligrams of molybdenum. Particularly, one has the 43 free from rhenium, the necessary presence of which was an unpleasant feature of the method previously used.

We have checked again the separations from Mo, Cb, and Zr and for all three elements less than one percent of the activity was found with the Mo, Cb or Zr fraction. . . .

We have investigated in a more quantitative way the precipitation of element 43 as a sulfide. In hydrochloric acid solution from 0.4 to 5 normal, using a few milligrams of platinum or rhenium as a carrier, the precipitation after 24 hours is complete. With 10 normal hydrochloric acid only a very small fraction of the total amount of 43 precipitates, whereas rhenium precipitates with a good yield, though slowly; similar results were obtained fusing arsenic as a carrier. We think that this property could be used for a fractional separation of 43 from rhenium or from other elements which precipitate with hydrogen sulfide even in very acid solution.

In an alkaline ammonia solution we have used manganese, iron and zinc as carriers. The precipitation with manganese seems to be fairly complete, somewhat less complete with iron and even less (order of magnitude of 25 percent) with zinc. . . .

The Triads

Group VIII

ELEMENT	ELECTRON SHELLS
$_{26}Fe$	$= K_2L_8M_{14}N_2$
$_{44}Ru$	$= K_2L_8M_{18}N_{15}O_1$
$_{76}Os$	$= K_2L_8M_{18}N_{32}O_{14}P_2$

ELEMENT	ELECTRON SHELLS
$_{27}Co$	$= K_2L_8M_{15}N_2$
$_{45}Rh$	$= K_2L_8M_{18}N_{16}O_1$
$_{77}Ir$	$= K_2L_8M_{18}N_{32}O_{17}$

ELEMENT	ELECTRON SHELLS
$_{28}Ni$	$= K_2L_8M_{16}N_2$
$_{46}Pd$	$= K_2L_8M_{18}N_{18}$
$_{78}Pt$	$= K_2L_8M_{18}N_{32}O_{17}P_1$

Grouping of three metals in the middle of each long series of elements into the eighth group triads is a somewhat arbitrary arrangement of the periodic table, but it remains a convenient one. Properties of Group VIII metals range from those of reactive iron, whose "rust doth corrupt," to stubborn platinum, the modern "noble" metal.

Iron, Cobalt, Nickel

→IRON follows copper and tin in order of discovery by ancient man, and the Iron Age is one of the epochs of pre-history distinguished by archaeologists. Cobalt and nickel were also known, but neither recognized nor appreciated, by early miners and artificers, who consigned them both to the devil. Old Nick and his imps, the kobolds, gave their names to the two metals, at first lumped together as "false copper."

Georg Brandt, about 1730, identified the metal in the well-known blue pigment, named it cobalt from the common name of the ore, and published the account in *Acta Literaria et Scientiarum Sveciae*, 1735. Axel Cronstedt distinguished nickel from cobalt, publishing his discoveries in *Vet. Acad. Handl. for* 1751 and 1754. A considerable discussion followed both discoveries, with confirmations and refutations by all the leading chemists of Europe.

To modern as well as to ancient scientists, the most interesting property of iron, cobalt and nickel is their magnetism. That of nickel is weak compared to iron, but cobalt has the ability to add to the magnetic strength of alloys containing it.

Literature on magnetism goes back to *De Magnete,* by Dr. William Gilbert of the court of Queen Elizabeth I., who summed up knowledge and lore of natural magnets. Discovery that a helix of copper wire which carries an electric current behaves like a bar magnet opened the modern phase of study of this mysterious quality. The "field" of magnetic "lines of force" surrounding either kind of magnet has given rise to new laws of physics, interpreted by new branches of mathematics. The energy used by molecular magnets lining themselves up with a magnetic field is used in a heat pump to bring such substances as liquid helium closer to the degree of cold approximating absolute zero.

Magnets give us electric currents, spin electric motors and pace atomic particles flying through cyclotrons. Bigger and stronger magnets are constantly being designed, and the magnetic qualities of all substances are being investigated. Some are found whose magnetism can be compared with that of iron. Notable among such substances is liquid oxygen!

Substances with strong magnetic properties, like iron and cobalt, are said to be ferro-magnetic. Others, whose attraction is many-fold weaker, but in the same direction, are called para-magnetic.

Other materials persistently set themselves cross-wise to the direction iron filings would take. The term for these is diamagnetic. This tendency, too, is very weak compared to the magnetism of iron.

The fact that our earth is a magnet, and that it spins on

its axis, leads to a parallel belief that magnetism arises from
the spin of atoms on their axes. This is in accord with many
observed phenomena. To explain iron's enormously strong
degree of magnetization, theory imagines rows of atomic magnets lined up so that they all point the same way. Their magnetic effects are believed thus to act in unison. These groupings
of atoms into magnetic "domains" behave as units when iron
is magnetized by influence of a magnetic field, or demagnetized
by heat or mechanical shock. They "flop" into cross-wise
positions, but can be brought back, by domain units, into
alignment again.

The theory is not completely worked out, but magnetic
quality is believed to originate in some of the inner electron
shells. Enough has been learned empirically about behavior of
materials so that magnetic alloys can now be made from non-
magnetic metals.

Ruthenium, Rhodium, Palladium

RUTHENIUM, *ein neues Metall der Platinerze (Ruthenium,
a new metal of the platinum ores), by Karl Karlovich Claus in
Annalen der Chemie und Pharmacie, Vol. 56, Heidelberg,
1846.*

→OSANN in the year 1828 described his researches on the
residues of Siberian platinum ores after treatment with aqua
regia and believed that he had discovered two metals, to one
of which he gave the name Pluranium and to the other Ruthenium. This research, which had no decisive result, has
been taken up again by Claus, and he has succeeded in finding a new metal in the platinum residues. To this he has given
the former name, although he separated it in smaller amount
than that mentioned by Osann. The substance called ruthenium oxide appears, according to Claus, to consist in great
part of silica, titanium oxide, iron oxide and zirconium oxide.

Claus treated the platinum residues in the following manner to obtain the new metal:

15 pounds of the platinum residues were melted with saltpeter (1 pound of the former to 2 pounds of the latter) in a
Hessian crucible, held in the melted state for two hours,
cooled and the pulverized mass extracted with water. The
brownish red solution contained (the quantities according to
the following order) chromium, osmium, silica, iridium, ruthenium, titanium, potassium also nitrous acid and free alkali.

The greater part of the new metal remained in the residue
after treatment of the melted mass with water. This residue
was put into a retort with half its amount of *aqua regia* and

some water and distilled almost to dryness, whereupon osmic acid distilled over into the receiver. The contents of the retort was extracted with water and the solution filtered. The undissolved material weighed 11½ pounds.

From the filtrate potassium carbonate threw down a mixture of iron oxide and ruthenium oxide; zinc precipitated some of the ruthenium out of the solution of the later in hydrochloric acid, another part remained with the iron and zinc oxides in the solution.

The brown alkaline solution, from which the two oxides were precipitated, after standing in a wooden container, became almost colorless. Concentrated potassium carbonate solution gave a white precipitate, turning brown upon drying but white again when re-precipitated. Hydrochloric acid threw down a metallic oxide with a greenish color, while titanium bearing silica clay remained undissolved. The hydrochloric acid solution after boiling with nitric acid became orange yellow; with hydrogen sulfide, blue.

The above alkaline solution was evaporated in an iron receptacle, whereupon much blue iridium oxide separated. The latter was dissolved in *aqua regia,* from the concentrated solution iridium was precipitated by potassium chloride, the mother liquor was evaporated to dryness and reduced with hydrogen. The metal powder so obtained consisted of iridium-ruthenium including a little rhodium.

This metal powder, as well as a part of the black powder insoluble in *aqua regia,* which still contained much iridium, chromic iron, silicate, ruthenium and rhodium, was once again ignited at white heat for two hours with the same amount of saltpeter, the cooled mass was extracted with distilled water and the orange-yellow solution mixed with a very little nitric acid, whereupon a voluminous, velvety black precipitate of impure, silica-containing potassium ruthenium oxide appeared.

The solution of this substance in concentrated hydrochloric acid, freed from silica by carefully evaporating it and taking it up again in water, was separated as potassium ruthenium chloride by addition of potassium chloride. It was recovered by evaporation. This salt is the material from which the metal and its still little known compounds can be prepared.

For isolation of the metal, this double salt was reduced with hydrogen; the metal remains, after extracting the potassium chloride with water, as a dark gray powder. (When reduced from the oxide it is light gray with a metallic luster). It is appreciably lighter than iridium; it changes, upon ignition in the air, into a blue-black oxide, which is not reduced at white heat. Upon fusing with acid potassium sulfate it is not dissolved. But upon fusing with saltpeter a dark green mass is formed which dissolves in water as potassium ruthenate, with the orange yellow color, from which acid the black ruthenium oxide is precipitated.

Caustic potash upon ignition dissolves the metal as readily as saltpeter. It is readily attacked by boiling with *aqua regia*, so that the liquid becomes brown, yet the greater part remains undissolved; a soluble compound of ruthenium chloride with potassium chloride ($Ru_2Cl_3 + 2KCl$) results when the metal mixed with potassium chloride is heated in a stream of chlorine gas.

Rhodium

ON A NEW METAL, *found in crude Platinum. By William Hyde Wollaston. In Transactions of the Royal Society, 1804.*
→ NOTWITHSTANDING I was aware that M. Descotils had ascribed the red color of certain precipitates and salts of platina to the presence of a new metal; and although Mr. Tennant had obligingly communicated to me his discovery of the same substance, as well as of a second new metal, in the shining powder that remains undissolved from the ore of platina; yet I was led to suppose that the more soluble parts of this mineral might be deserving of further examination, as the fluid which remains after the precipitation of platina by sal ammoniac presents appearances which I could not ascribe to either of those bodies, or to any other known substance.

My inquiries having terminated more successfully than I had expected, I design in the present memoir to prove the existence, and to examine the properties, of another metal, hitherto unknown, which may not improperly be distinguished by the name of *rhodium,* from the rose-color of a dilute solution of the salts containing it. . . .

The color of the solution that remains after the precipitation of platina varies, not only according to its state of dilution, but also according to the strength and proportions of the nitric and muriatic acids employed. This color, though principally owing to the quantity of iron contained in it, arises also in part from a small quantity of the ammoniaco-muriate of platina that necessarily remains dissolved, and from other metals contained in still smaller proportions.

To recover the remaining platina, as well as to separate the other metals that are present from the iron, I have in some experiments employed zinc, in others iron, for their precipitation. The former appears preferable, but, when the latter has been used, the precipitate may immediately be freed from the iron that adheres to it, by muriatic acid, without the loss of any of those metals which are at present the subject of inquiry. . . . ,

To the solution [in nitric acid] were added 20 grains of common salt; and, when the whole had been evaporated to dryness with a very gentle heat, the residuum, which I had found from prior experiments, would consist of the soda-muriates of platina, of palladium, and of rhodium, was washed repeatedly with small quantities of alcohol, till it came off nearly colorless. There remained a triple salt of rhodium, which by these means is freed from all metallic impurities.

Palladium

An Account of EXPERIMENTS MADE ON PALLADIUM, *found in combination with pure Gold. By Joseph Cloud, an Officer in the Mint of the United States. In Transactions of the American Philosophical Society, Vol. 6, Philadelphia, [dated] 1804. (Paper read June 23, 1809).*

➤ NOTWITHSTANDING the numerous experiments that have been made by several eminent chemists, on a metallic substance, discovered by Doctor Wollaston, in combination with crude platinum, and by him called palladium; there still remains much doubt with respect to the existence of such a simple substance. Professor Murray, one of the latest writers on chemistry, in speaking of palladium, and other metals found in combination with crude platinum, says: "It is not impossible that they may be alloys of others; or that the peculiar properties which they appear to exhibit, may arise from combinations which analysis has not detected. The peculiarity of their association in one natural production, while there are no traces of them in any other, perhaps lends force to this supposition." It has been my fortune, however, to obtain it from a different source; which enables me to point out some of its characteristics, that will throw such light on the subject, as to remove all doubts respecting the existence of this simple metal.

On the 15th of May, 1807, a deposit of gold bullion, from Brazil, in South America, was made at the Mint of the United States, weighing 797 ounces, 4 dwts., gross, equal to 819 oz. 11 dwts. 11 grs. standard. It was composed of about 120 small ingots, differing in weight; each of them was stamped on one side with the arms of Portugal, and the inscription of "Rio das Mortes." The other side was stamped with a globe. They were also marked with their respective qualities. Among them were two or three ingots, so remarkably different in color from any of the common native alloys of gold, that I was induced to reserve one, weighing 3 ounces, 11 dwts., 12 grains, for examination, and which was subjected to the following experiments. . . .

[*The cupellation tests for gold.*]

By these preliminary experiments I discovered, that the alloy was a compound of gold, and a metal that would resist the cupel, and was soluble in the nitric and nitro-muriatic acids.

Palladium is of a greyish-white color; so closely resembling that of platinum, that they cannot be distinguished by their complexion. It is malleable, and very ductile; so that by the rolling-mill it can be reduced to thin plates. In hardness it is nearly equal to wrought iron. Its specific gravity, at 64° F., is $11^{44}/_{99}$. It may be alloyed with a number of the metals. With gold, silver, and platinum, it forms ductile alloys, and very much debases the color of the two former.

It would be useless here to go into a further detail of the characters and properties of palladium, as Dr. Wollaston and Mr. Chenevix have fully explained them, in the Philosophical Transactions of the Royal Society of London, for 1803-4 and 5. It is enough for me to have shown, I trust satisfactorily, that palladium has a real existence; that it is one of the pure or inoxidable metals; and, in this respect, on a par with gold, silver, and platinum; and that it has been found in a native combination with gold; without the presence of platinum, or any other metal.

This confirmation of the existence of palladium was a feather in the cap of the youthful United States Mint.

Osmium, Iridium, Platinum

DISCOVERY OF TWO NEW METALS IN CRUDE PLATINA. *By Smithson Tennant, esq., F.R.S., in Nicholson's Journal of Natural Philosophy, Chemistry and the Arts, Vol. 8, London, 1804.*

→ AT THE LAST meeting of the Royal Society a paper of Mr. Tennant was read, on the analysis of the black powder which remains after dissolving platina, showing that it contains two new metals. Mr. Tennant's first experiments were made last summer, and had been communicated to Sir Joseph Banks, after which an account of one of these metals appeared in France, by M. Descotils and also by M. Vauquelin.

The properties ascribed to it by the French chemists are, 1. That it reddens the precipitates of platina made by sal ammoniac; 2. That it dissolves in marine acid; 3. That it is precipitated by galls and prussiate of potash.

The properties mentioned by Mr. Tennant are, that it dissolves in all the acids, but least in marine acid, with which it forms octahedral crystals. The solution with much oxygen is deep red, with a smaller proportion green or deep blue. It is partially precipitated by the three alkalies when pure. All the metals, excepting gold and platina, precipitate it.

Galls and precipitate of potash take away the color of this solution, but without any precipitate, and afford an easy test of its presence. The oxide therefore loses its oxygen, by water alone. . . .

As the French chemists have not given a name to the metal, Mr. Tennant inclines to call it *Iridium*, from the various colors of it in solution.

The second new metal is obtained by heating the black powder with pure alkali in a silver crucible. The oxide of this metal unites with the alkali, and may be expelled by an acid and obtained by distillation, being very volatile.

The oxide has a very strong smell, from which Mr. Tennant has called it *Osmium*. It does not redden vegetable blues, but stains the skin to a deep red or black. The oxide in solution with water has no color, but by combining with alkali or lime becomes yellow. With galls it gives a very vivid blue color.

All the metals, excepting gold and platina, precipitate this metal. If mercury is agitated with the aqueous solution of the oxide, an amalgam is formed, which, by heat, loses the mercury, and leaves the osmium pure as a black powder.

Platinum

A VOYAGE TO SOUTH AMERICA, *by Jorge Juan and Antonio de Ulloa. London, 1772.*

➤ IN THE DISTRICT of Choco are many mines of Lavadero, or wash gold, like those we have just described. There are also some, where mercury must be used, the gold being enveloped in other metallic bodies, stones, and bitumens. Several of the mines have been abandoned on account of the platina; a substance of such resistance that when struck on an anvil of steel, it is not easy to be separated; nor is it calcinable; so that the metal, inclosed within this obdurate body, could not be extracted without infinite labor and charge.

List of Chemical Elements

ATOMIC NO.	SYMB.	NAME	ATOMIC* WEIGHT	ISOTOPES

0 n ncutron
Initiates nuclear fission.

1 H Hydrogen 1.0080 1, 2
The nucleus of the hydrogen atom is the proton, standard for weight of subatomic particles. Hydrogen gas is used for the inflation of balloons. The artificially radioactive H3 isotope with a half life of 12.4 years, called tritium, is important in the fusion or hydrogen bomb. Isotope H2 is called deuterium.

2 He Helium 4.003 3, 4
Used for airship inflation. At temperature near absolute zero, exhibits fourth state of matter.

3 Li Lithium 6.940 6, 7
Red flame. Hydride gives off H.

4 Be Beryllium 9.013 9
Neutron source under atomic bombardment. Possible moderator for atomic bomb. Minerals are jewels. Poison.

5 B Boron 10.82 10, 11
Control rods for atomic reactor. Borax for flux. Boric acid.

6 C Carbon 12.010 12, 13
Compounds comprise organic chemistry. Diamond hardest substance is pure C. In coal, oil, natural gas, C is energy source. CO_2 in atmosphere, product of respiration, used in photosynthesis. C-14 radioactive half-life 5900 years (created from N by cosmic rays) provides atomic calendar for archaeological dating. Atomic weight probably low by 0.001.

7 N Nitrogen 14.008 14, 15
Present in protein "life" compounds, explosives, atmosphere, fertilizer, urea. Atomic weight probably high by 0.0005.

8 O Oxygen 16 16, 17, 18
International atomic weights are defined with O as 16 as the basis of the chemical scale. Official table therefore shows round figure. O is used in breathing, combustion. Atmosphere of oxygen may be unique on earth.

9 F Fluorine 19.00 19
Use in atomic energy materials has developed its large-scale production. Etches glass. Poison.

10 Ne Neon 20.183 20, 21, 22
Red in gas discharge as in advertising signs.

11 Na Sodium 22.997 23
Present almost everywhere. In common table salt, soap, etc. Atomic weight probably slightly high, probable best value between 22.990 and 22.994.

12 Mg Magnesium 24.32 24, 25, 26
Light-weight metal, used in alloys. Extracted from seawater. Powder explodes as flashlight. Essential in chlorophyll. Becoming widely used as an industrial chemical component. Alloys are finding many structural uses where low density is important.

* Atomic weights have been corrected to agree with those given in J. Am. Chem. Soc. 78, 3235 (1956)—"Report on Atomic Weights for 1954-55" by Edward Wichers.

Atomic No.	Symb.	Name	Atomic Weight	Isotopes
13	Al	Aluminum	26.98	27

Light weight metal. Prevalent in clays. Alums. Mordant for dyes in textile industry.

| 14 | Si | Silicon | 28.09 | 28, 29, 30 |

In rocks, sand, slag, cement, glass, ceramics.

| 15 | P | Phosphorus | 30.975 | 31 |

Essential in living cells, major fertilizer element, as element used as incendiary weapon.

| 16 | S | Sulfur | 32.066 | 32, 33, 34, 36 |

Widely distributed, occurs as element, volcanoes may be due to this element. Sulfuric acid major chemical material. Because of natural variations in the relative abundances of isotopes, atomic weight has range of ±0.003.

| 17 | Cl | Chlorine | 35.457 | 35, 37 |

Combines with most elements. In seawater. NaCl is common salt, AgCl used in photography. Element is corrosive poisonous gas.

| 18 | A | Argon | 39.944 | 36, 38, 40 |

Most plentiful rare gas. White light in gaseous discharge tube. Used as blanket for chemical reactions to exclude air.

| 19 | K | Potassium | 39.100 | 39, *40*, 41 |

Vegetable alkali, in fertilizer, soap.

| 20 | Ca | Calcium | 40.08 | 40, 42, 43, 44, 46, 48 |

In lime, cement, limestone, ceramics, fertilizer. Good neutron absorber.

| 21 | Sc | Scandium | 44.96 | 45 |
| 22 | Ti | Titanium | 47.90 | 46, 47, 48, 49, 50 |

Light-weight non-corrosive metal, plentiful in earth's crust. Oxide is white pigment.

| 23 | V | Vanadium | 50.95 | 51 |

Alloy in tool steel.

| 24 | Cr | Chromium | 52.01 | 50, 52, 53, 54 |

Metal used in electroplating. Compounds as green and yellow pigments.

| 25 | Mn | Manganese | 54.93 | 55 |

Alloying for tool steel, oxidizing agent. Atomic weight probably low by 0.01.

| 26 | Fe | Iron | 55.85 | 54, 56, 57, 58 |

Most useful metal. Can be magnetized. In hemoglobin, red cells of blood.

| 27 | Co | Cobalt | 58.94 | 59 |

Used for plating. Can be magnetized. Blue pigments, which turn pink, used for humidity indicator.

| 28 | Ni | Nickel | 58.69 | 58, 60, 61, 62, 64 |

Decorative metal for electroplating.

| 29 | Cu | Copper | 63.54 | 63, 65 |

Probably earliest metal, occurring native. Used for electrical properties, corrosion resistance, in coinage.

| 30 | Zn | Zinc | 65.38 | 64, 66, 67, 68, 70 |

Used for galvanizing sheet iron, in dry batteries, ZnO as pigment. Brass alloy with copper.

| 31 | Ga | Gallium | 69.72 | 69, 71 |

Metal melts in hand, wets glass.

| 32 | Ge | Germanium | 72.60 | 70, 72, 73, 74, 76 |

Used in transistor, successor to electron tube as amplifier. Semi-conductor.

| 33 | As | Arsenic | 74.91 | 75 |

Poison.

| 34 | Se | Selenium | 78.96 | 74, 76, 77, 78, 80, 82 |

Photoelectric. Poison, in plants affecting cattle.

ATOMIC No.	SYMB.	NAME	ATOMIC WEIGHT	ISOTOPES
35	Br	Bromine	79.916	79, 81

Used in photography and medicine. Obtained from sea water.

36	Kr	Krypton	83.80	78, 80, 82, 83, 84, 86
37	Rb	Rubidium	85.48	85, 87
38	Sr	Strontium	87.63	84, 86, 87, 88

Red flame used in flares.

| 39 | Y | Yttrium | 88.92 | 89 |
| 40 | Zr | Zirconium | 91.22 | 90, 91, 92, 94, 96 |

Occurs in zircon gems, important atomic reactor structural material because of low neutron absorption cross section, exceptional corrosion resistance and strength at high temperatures.

| 41 | Nb (Cb) | Niobium (Columbium) | 92.91 | 93 |

While niobium is the name officially adopted, both symbol and name of columbium are still widely used, especially in America.

| 42 | Mo | Molybdenum | 95.95 | 92, 94, 95, 96, 97, 98, 100 |

Used in alloy steels for tools.

| 43 | Tc | Technetium | [99] | |

Fission product. No stable isotope. Occurs in the stars.

44	Ru	Ruthenium	101.7	96, 98, 99, 100, 101, 102, 104
45	Rh	Rhodium	102.91	103
46	Pd	Palladium	106.7	102, 104, 105, 106, 108, 110

Used in jewelry as platinum substitute.

| 47 | Ag | Silver | 107.880 | 107, 109 |

Used in jewelry, coinage, photography. Good conductor of electricity.

| 48 | Cd | Cadmium | 112.41 | 106, 108, 110, 111, 112, 113, 114, 116 |

Oxide is yellow pigment.

| 49 | In | Indium | 114.76 | 113, 115 |

Used in radiation detection badges.

| 50 | Sn | Tin | 118.70 | 112, 114, 115, 116, 117, 118, 119, 120, 122, *124* |

Used as protective coating on sheet iron. Bronze alloy with copper.

| 51 | Sb | Antimony | 121.76 | 121, 123 |

Used in type metal. Salts used in textile industry.

| 52 | Te | Tellurium | 127.61 | 120, 122, 123, 124, 125, 126, 128, 130 |
| 53 | I | Iodine | 126.91 | 127 |

Used as antiseptic in medicine.

54	Xe	Xenon	131.3	124, 126, 128, 129, 130, 131, 132, 134, 136
55	Cs	Cesium	132.91	133
56	Ba	Barium	137.36	130, 132, 134, 135, 136, 137, 138

Oxide white pigment. Used to precipitate sulfates.

| 57 | La | Lanthanum | 138.92 | 138, 139 |

Atomic No.	Symb.	Name	Atomic Weight	Isotopes
58	Ce	Cerium	140.13	136, 138, 140, 142
		Used in "flints" for lighters.		
59	Pr	Praseodymium	140.92	141
60	Nd	Neodymium	144.27	142, 143, 144, 145, 146, 148, 150
61	Pm	Promethium	[145]	
		Fission product. Does not exist in nature.		
62	Sm	Samarium	150.43	144, 147, 148, 149, 150, 152, 154
63	Eu	Europium	152.0	151, 153
64	Gd	Gadolinium	156.9	152, 154, 155, 156, 157, 158, 160
65	Tb	Terbium	159.2	159
		Best value atomic weight near 158.9.		
66	Dy	Dysprosium	162.46	156, 158, 160, 161, 162, 163, 164
67	Ho	Holmium	164.94	165
68	Er	Erbium	167.2	162, 164, 166, 167, 168, 170
69	Tm	Thulium	169.4	169
		Best value atomic weight near 169.0.		
70	Yb	Ytterbium	173.04	168, 170, 171, 172, 173, 174, 176
71	Lu	Lutetium	174.99	175, *176*
72	Hf	Hafnium	178.6	174, 176, 177, 178, 179, 180
73	Ta	Tantalum	180.88	181
		Used in surgery.		
74	W	Tungsten	183.92	180, 182, 183, 184, 186
		Also officially named wolfram, which is preferred name in non-English speaking countries but which has failed to gain acceptance in the United States. Used as incandescent lamp filaments.		
75	Re	Rhenium	186.31	185, *187*
76	Os	Osmium	190.2	184, 186, 187, 188, 189, 190, 192
77	Ir	Iridium	193.1	191, 193
		Used as platinum substitute. Best value atomic weight near 192.2.		
78	Pt	Platinum	195.23	190, 192, 194, 195, 196, 198
		Used for jewelry, laboratory ware.		
79	Au	Gold	197.2	197
		Used for jewelry, monetary standard, medicine, photography. Best value atomic weight near 197.0		
80	Hg	Mercury	200.61	196, 198, 199, 200, 201, 202, 204
		Liquid metal at ordinary temperatures. Used for thermometers, amalgams, heat transfer. Poison. Compounds used in medicine.		
81	Tl	Thallium	204.39	203, 205, *206, 207, 208, 210*
		Used for rat poison.		

Atomic No.	Symb.	Name	Atomic Weight	Isotopes
82	Pb	Lead	207.21	204, 206, 207, 208, 210, 211, 212, 214

Soft metal, used in plumbing, paint pigment as oxides. Natural disintegration product of radium and heavier radioactive elements. Accumulative poison. Used for shield against radiations.

| 83 | Bi | Bismuth | 209.00 | 209, 210, 211, 212, 214 |

Salts used in medical radiography. Makes low melting point alloys.

84	Po	Polonium	210	210, 211, 212, 214, 215, 216, 218
85	At	Astatine	[210]	218
86	Rn	Radon	222	219, 220, 222

Em, emanation, is the name coming into use for element 86, heavy inert gas radioactive product of heavier elements, with radon designating that from radium, thoron that from thorium and acton that from actinium.

| 87 | Fr | Francium | [223] | 223 |
| 88 | Ra | Radium | 226.05 | 223, 224, 226, 228 |

Source of most of our information about radioactivity, used in medicine and industry for its radiations.

| 89 | Ac | Actinium | 227 | 227, 228 |
| 90 | Th | Thorium | 232.12 | 227, 228, 230, 231, 232, 234 |

Came into commercial use for gas mantles. Oxide is a refractory material. Element can supplement uranium as nuclear fuel.

| 91 | Pa | Protactinium | 231 | 231, 234 |
| 92 | U | Uranium | 238.07 | 234, 235, 238 |

Isotope 235 fissionable. Source of atomic bomb material.

| 93 | Np | Neptunium | [237] | |
| 94 | Pu | Plutonium | [242] | |

Pu-239 fissionable. Made from uranium 238. Atomic bomb material.

95	Am	Americium	[241]	
96	Cm	Curium	[248]	
97	Bk	Berkelium	[249]	
98	Cf	Californium	[249]	
99	Es*	Einsteinium	[254]	
100	Fm	Fermium	[255]	
101	Md*	Mendelevium	[256]	
102	No	Nobelium*	[254]	

* The symbols Es and Md for elements 99 and 101 were recommended by the Commission but have not been accepted by the discoverers who prefer E and Mv. The name and symbol of element 102 is in dispute (see text.)

Symbols, names, and chemical atomic weights are those adopted by the Commission on Atomic Weights of the International Union of Pure and Applied Chemistry at Zurich, in July, 1955. It should be noted that this chemical atomic weight scale is not identical to the physical atomic weight scale. In the physical atomic weight scale the mass of O¹⁶ is taken as the standard and is assigned the mass of exactly 16.00000 units; in the chemical scale the atomic weight of the natural isotopic mixture of oxygen (containing small amounts of O^{17} and O^{18}) is assigned the value of exactly 16.00000. Conversions to the physical scale can be made by dividing by 1.000275. Several suggestions for unifying the two scales have been made. A scale based on fluorine 19 (fluorine has no other known natural isotopes) appears to be the most attractive. No such changeover, however, is likely to occur soon owing to the large amount of data in textbooks, reference books, etc. that would require revision.

For the transuranium elements, the best system for selecting a mass number to serve as the atomic weight would combine the criteria of availability and long half life. (The mass numbers given in brackets have been selected in this way.)

Chronology of the Elements

Earliest found:
Carbon
Sulfur
Seven metals of
the ancients:
Gold—Sun
Silver—Moon
Copper—Venus
Iron—Mars
Tin—Jupiter
Lead—Saturn
Mercury—Mercury
Medieval discoveries:
Zinc
Arsenic
Bismuth
Modern times:
1604 Antimony
1669 Phosphorus
1737 Cobalt
1748 Platinum
1751 Nickel
1772 Nitrogen
1774 Oxygen
1774 Chlorine
1774 Manganese
1781 Molybdenum
1783 Telurium
1783 Tungsten
1789 Uranium
1789 Zirconium
1790 Hydrogen
1791 Titanium
1794 Yttrium

1798 Beryllium
1798 Chromium
1801 Columbium
1802 Tantalum
1803 Rhodium
1803 Palladium
1803 Cerium
1804 Osmium
1804 Iridium
1807 Sodium
1807 Potassium
1808 Boron
1808 Magnesium
1808 Calcium
1808 Strontium
1808 Barium
1811 Iodine
1817 Cadmium
1817 Lithium
1818 Selenium
1824 Indium
1824 Silicon
1826 Bromine
1827 Aluminum
1829 Thorium
1830 Vanadium
1839 Lanthanum
1843 Erbium
1843 Terbium
1844 Ruthenium
1860 Cesium
1861 Rubidium
1861 Thallium
1875 Gallium
1878 Holmium

1878 Ytterbium
1879 Samarium
1879 Thulium
1879 Scandium
1880 Gadolinium
1885 Praseodymium
1885 Neodymium
1886 Germanium
1886 Dysprosium
1886 Fluorine
1894 Argon
1895 Helium
1898 Neon
1898 Krypton
1898 Xenon
1898 Polonium
1898 Radium
1899 Actinium
1900 Radon
1901 Europium
1907 Lutetium
1917 Protactinium
1923 Hafnium
1925 Rhenium
1932 neutron
1937 Technetium
1939 Francium
1940 Astatine
1940 Neptunium
1940 Plutonium
1944 Americium
1944 Curium
1947 Promethium
1949 Berkelium
1950 Californium
1952 Einsteinium
1953 Fermium
1955 Mendelevium
1957 Nobelium

Glossary of Old Chemical Terms

Acidium salis—hydrochloric acid
Aer fixus—carbon dioxide
Aerial acid—carbon dioxide
Alkali fixum—sodium hydroxide
Alkali volatile—ammonium hydroxide
Alum—aluminum sulfate (other crystalline salts were also called alums)
Alumine—alumina (Al_2O_3)
Aqua fortis—nitric acid
Aqua regia (regis)—mixture of nitric and hydrochloric acids
Ammoniac—ammonia
Argentum (Ag)—silver
Aurum (Au)—gold
Aurum fulminans—"explosive gold" made by precipitating gold chloride with ammonium hydroxide.
Barane, calcane, magnesane, strontane—Davy's nomenclature for chlorides of Ba, Ca, Mg, Sr.
Bore—boron
Calcia—calcium oxide, lime
Calx—lime, earthy oxide of other metal
Copper (blue) vitriol—cupric sulfate
Corrosive sublimate—mercuric chloride
Cuprum—copper
Dephlogisticated air—oxygen (Priestley)
Empyreal air—oxygen (Scheele)
Equivalent—atomic mass
Ferrum (Fe)—iron
Fossil—mineral
Galls, gallic acid—tannic acid derived from galls on oak bark
Hydrargyrum (Hg)—mercury
Hydro-sulphuret—hydrogen sulfide
Inflammable air—hydrogen
Iron (green) vitriol—ferrous sulfate
Jargon—zircon
Kalium (K)—potassium
Latane, lantan—lanthanum
Lime—calcium oxide, hydroxide

Lixiviate—extract with water
Lute—temporary cement for apparatus
Magnium—magnesium
Marine acid—hydrochloric acid
Matrass—retort
Mephitis—nitrogen
Mercurius sublimatus—mercuric chloride
Mineral alkali—sodium hydroxide
Muriatic acid—hydrochloric acid
Muriate—chloride
Natron (Na)—sodium
Noctiluca—phosphorus
Oil of vitriol—sulfuric acid
Phlogiston—principle of oxidation
Plumbago—graphite
Plumbum (Pb)—lead
Potash—potassium, also its hydroxide and carbonate
Prussiate of potash—potassium cyanide
Prussic acid—hydrocyanic acid
Quicklime—calcium oxide
Quicksilver—mercury
Sal ammoniac—ammonium chloride
Sal commune—sodium chloride
Saltpeter—potassium nitrate
Silex—silica, silicon dioxide
Slaked lime—calcium hydroxide
Stannum (Sn)—tin
Stibium (Sb)—antimony
Sugar of lead—lead acetate
Sulphuret—sulfide
Sulphuretted hydrogen—hydrogen sulfide
Tartar—potassium carbonate in early writings. Modern tartaric acid is $COOH(CHOH)_2COOH$
Vegetable alkali—potassium hydroxide
Vegetation—crystals resembling leaves
Vital air—oxygen (Lavoisier)
Vitriol, oil of—sulfuric acid
Zinc (white) vitriol—zinc sulfate

Index